Through the Ages

On 8th March 1936, readers of the Sunday Post Fun Section encountered a small lad sitting on his bucket before being welcomed in to number 10 Glebe Street for the very first time. Over 80 years later, this wee boy from Auchenshoogle and Scotland's happiest family from Auchentogle continue to make readers laugh every weekend.

The world has changed a lot over the past eight decades, but The Broons and Oor Wullie have endured, remaining a firm symbol of community, celebrating Scottish tradition and family values with a little bit of mischief along the way. Despite the warm comforts of these classic strips, The Broons and Oor Wullie have continually adapted to the decades, reflecting the cultural and historic changes they were faced with, from fashion trends to the Second World War.

This classic collection showcases some of the very best strips, exploring the changes these characters have faced, and reminding us all why The Broons and Oor Wullie continue to raise smiles of Scots across the country to this very day.

© DCT Consumer Products (UK) Ltd 2017
D.C. Thomson and Co. Ltd,
185 Fleet Street,
London EC4A 2HS

Printed in China

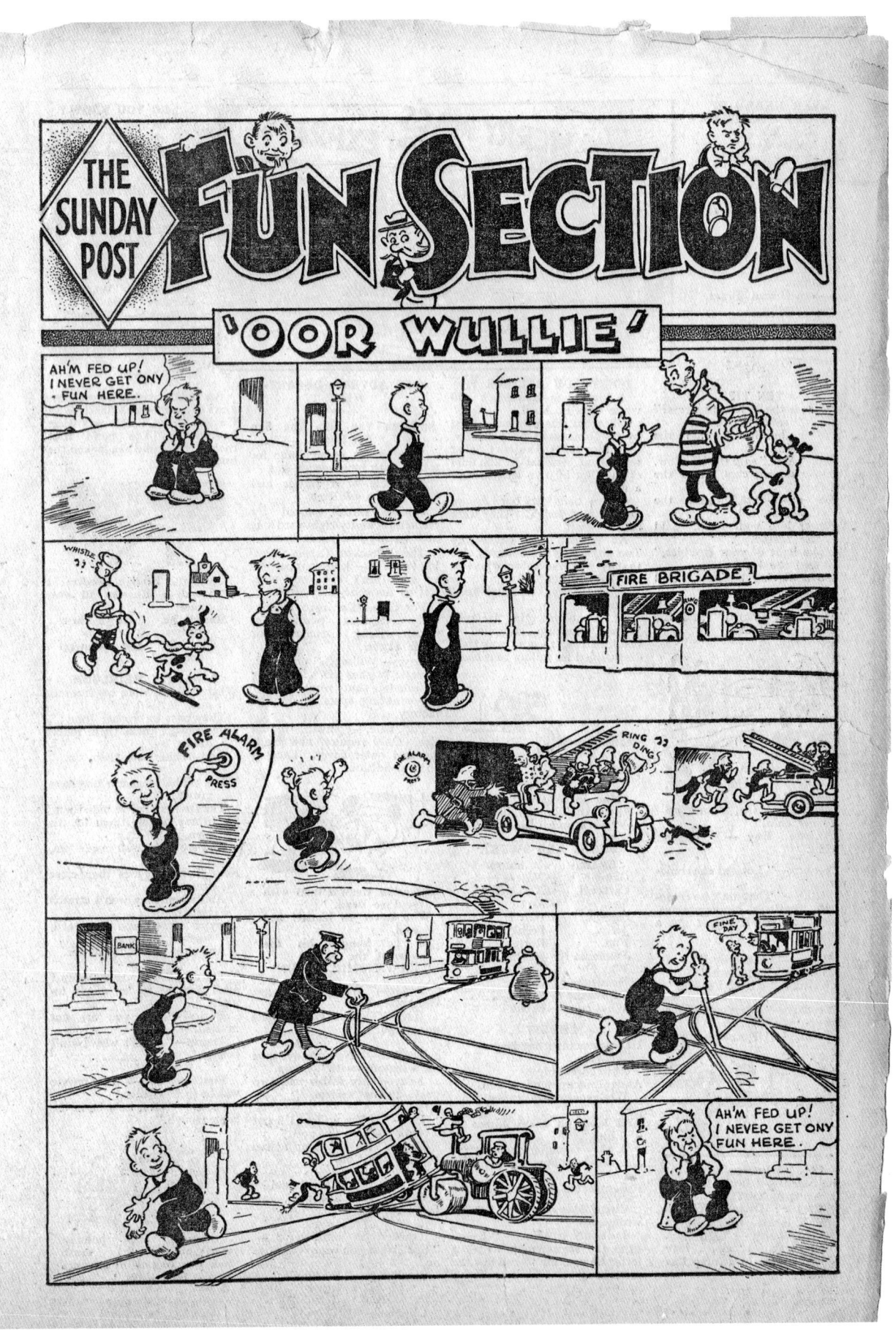

Oor Wullie was the cover star of the Sunday Post's Fun Section from his very first appearance. This brilliant strip gave Wullie the perfect introduction to boys and girls across the country with plenty of mischief and mayhem, and his trusty bucket in tow.

This snapshot of the Broon family gave readers of the Fun Section a braw chance to meet the characters. This chaotic photo finish gave readers a succinct introduction to the characters, proving that even the happiest of families can have moments of calamity.

A Boy and his Bucket

Where would Oor Wullie be without his bucket? In every comic strip since 8th March 1936, the stories have started and ended with Wullie's trusty bucket.

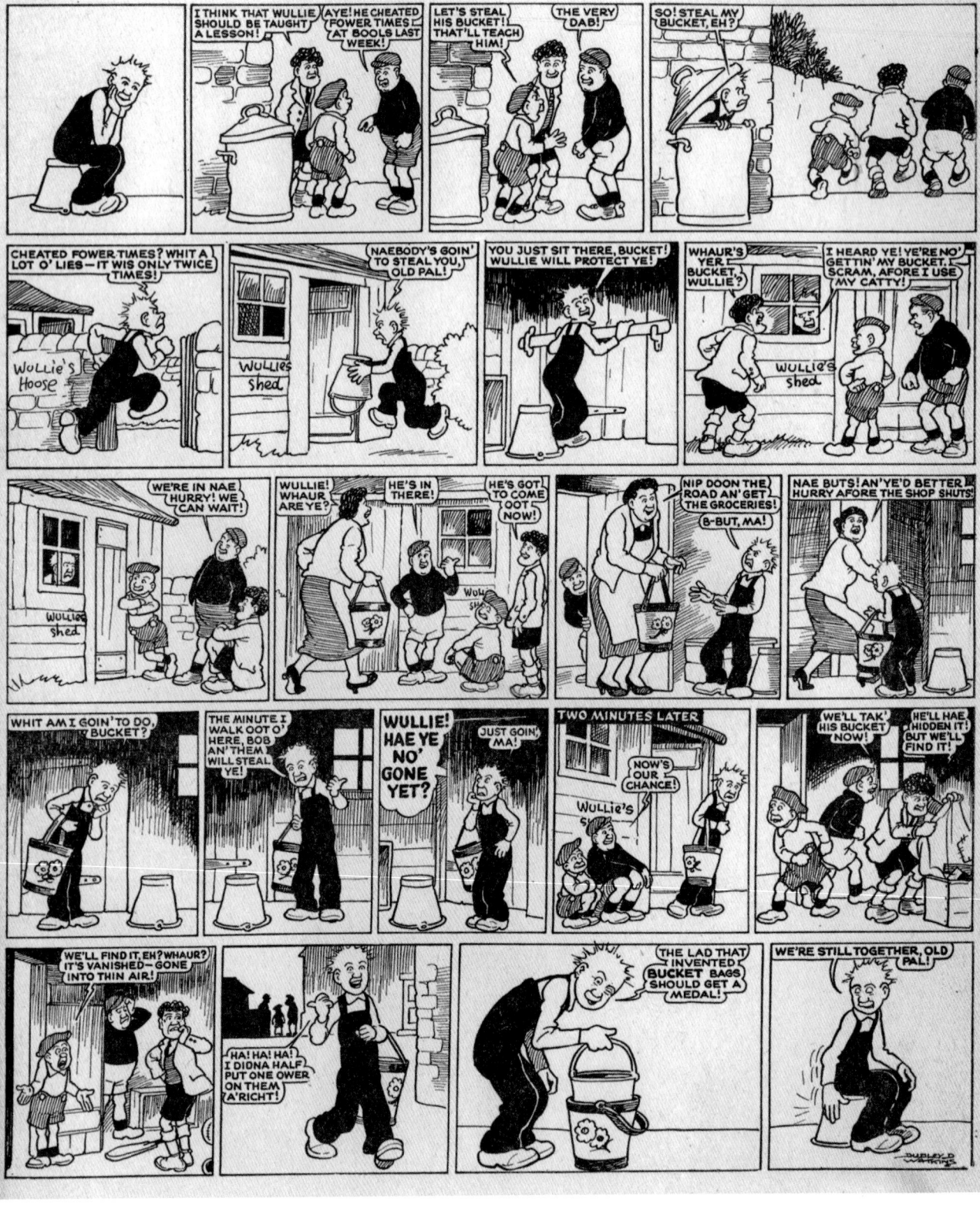

10 Glebe Street

One of the most endearing features of The Broons is the warmth and calamity found in a family home, which often feels all too familiar. The comedic portrayal of an ordinary family is just one reason as to why the doors to Glebe Street have remained open for so long.

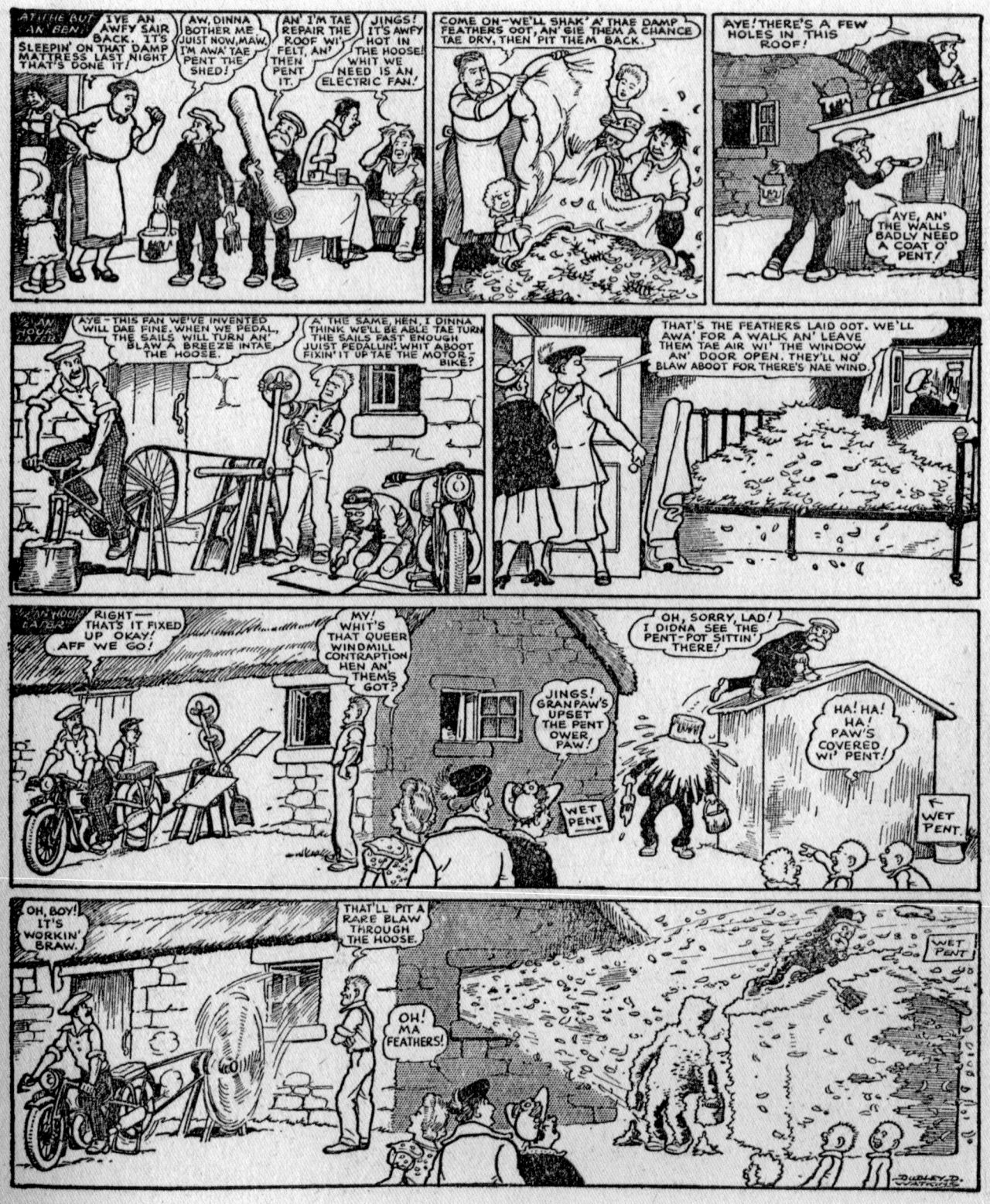

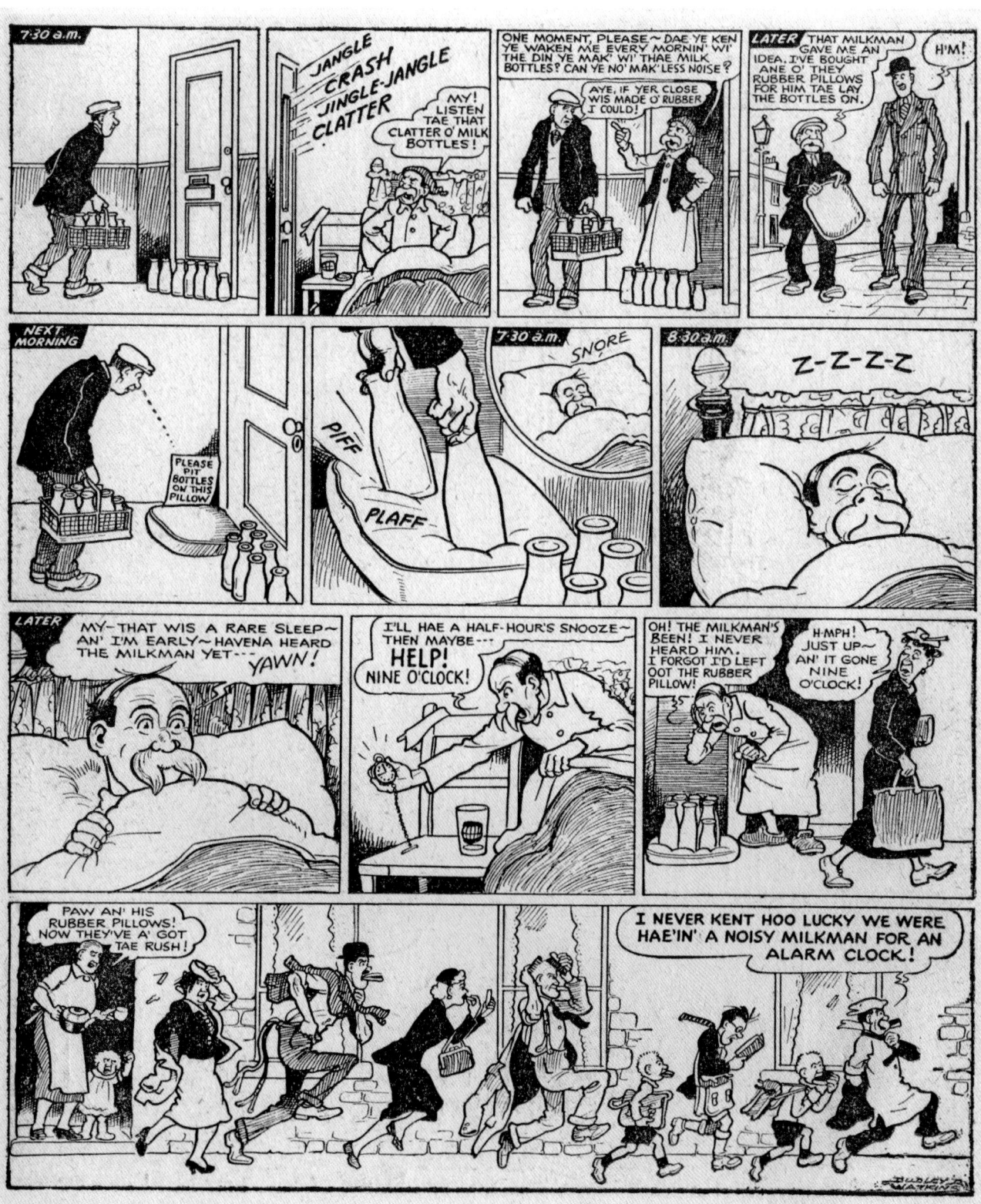

Granpaw Broon

Granpaw Broon quickly established himself as a fan favourite, with his wily tricks and quick wit. However, the auld character hasn't always been part of the cast, originally only making cameo appearances in the background in photo frames. It was not until 1938 that he appeared more regularly.

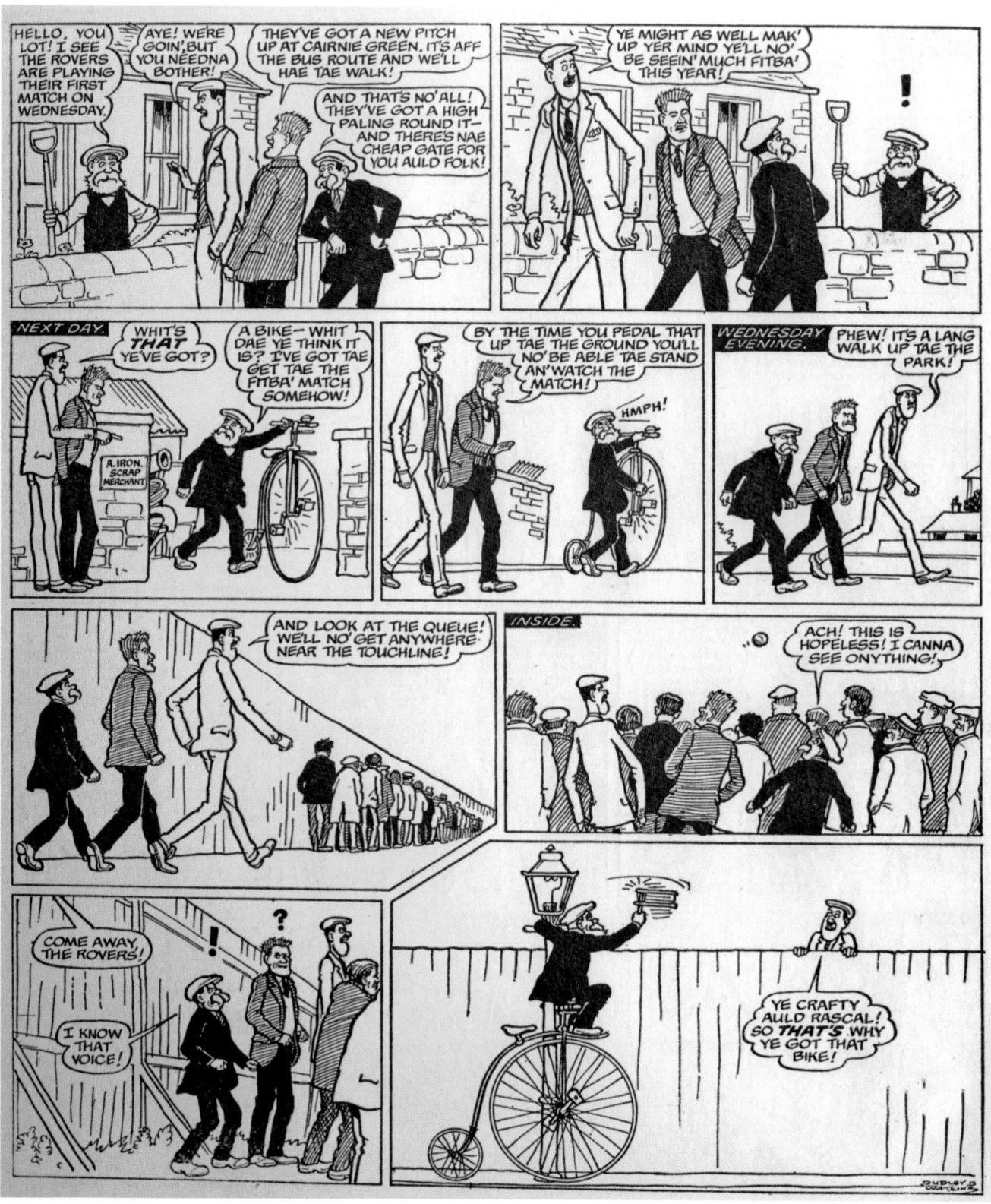

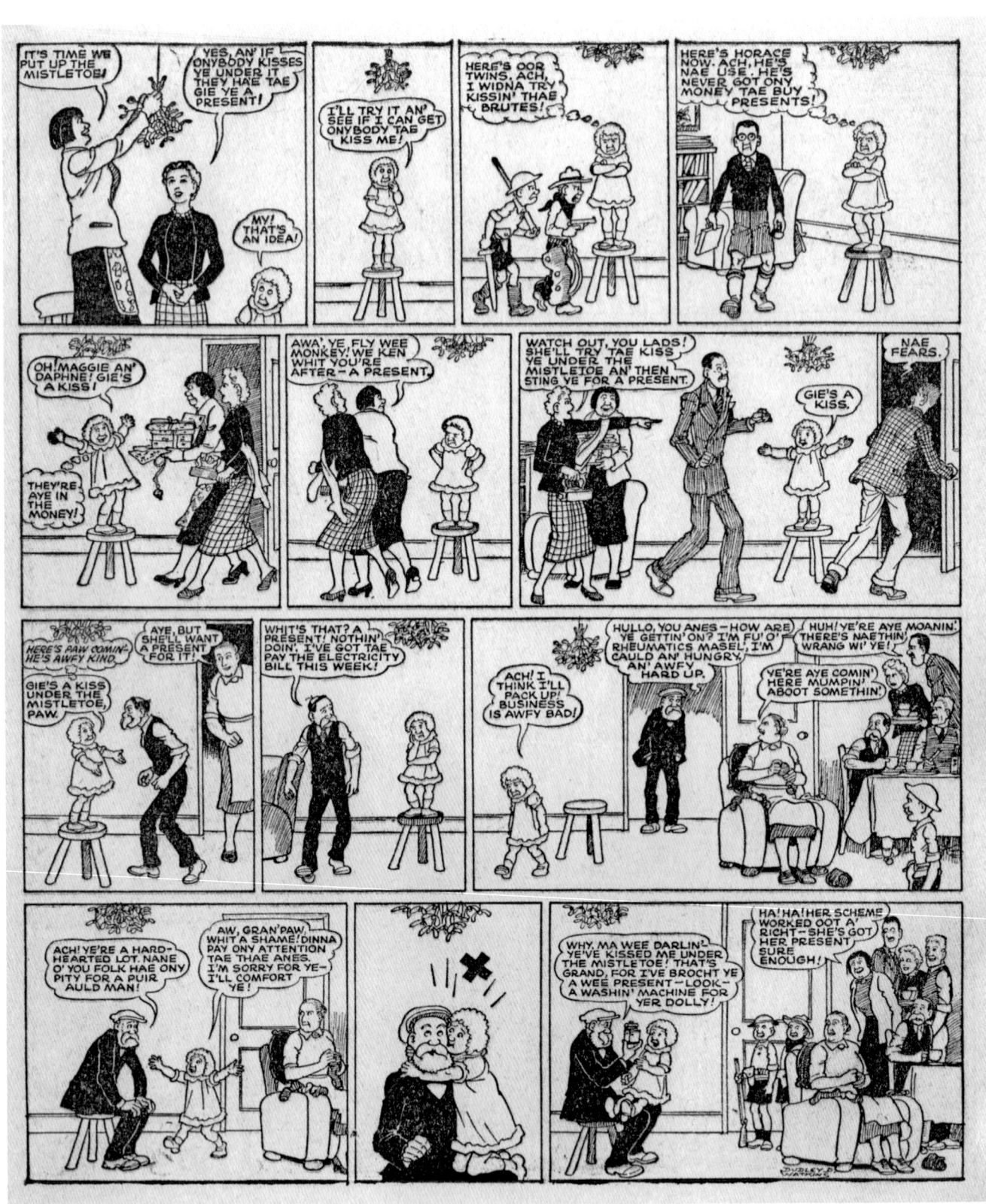

'Mah Wee Lamb'

Perhaps no two family members have a closer bond than Granpaw Broon and his wee lamb, the Bairn. Partners in crime, the two often work together to best the family. With such a mentor, it's no surprise the Bairn is wiser than her years.

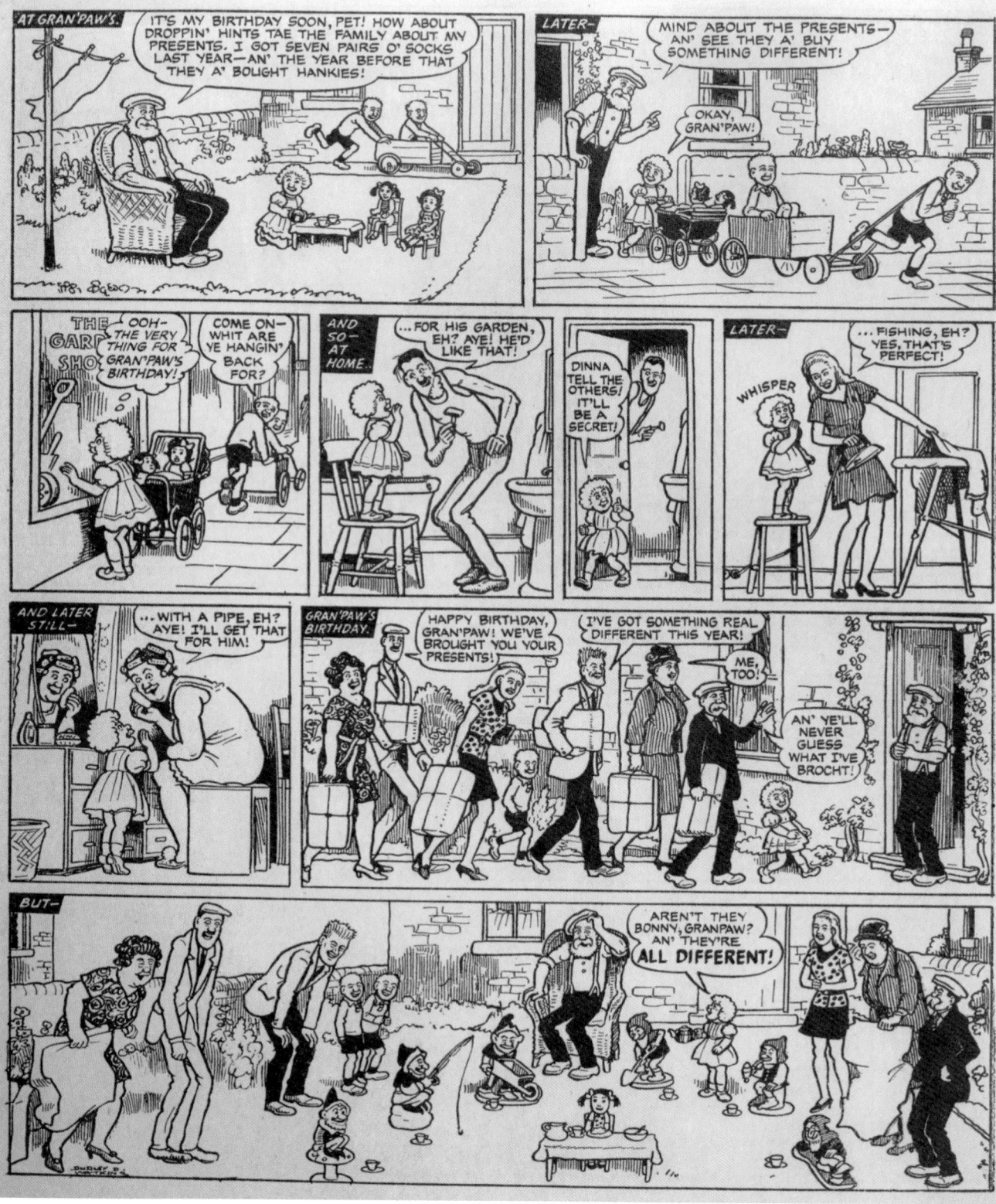

Incredible Icons

Over the past eight decades, The Broons and Oor Wullie have made the most of fashion trends, from heinous haircuts to unflattering jumpers.

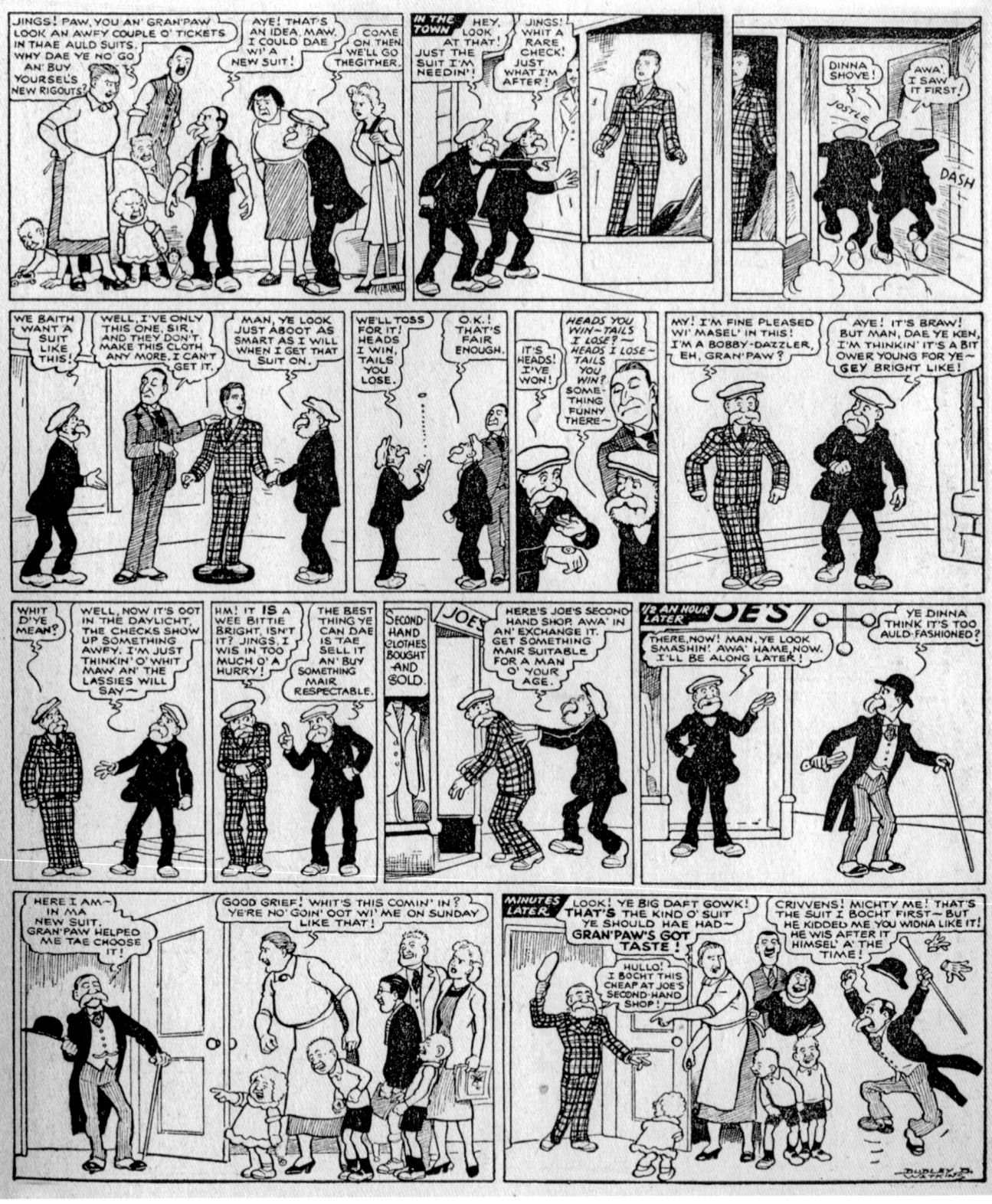

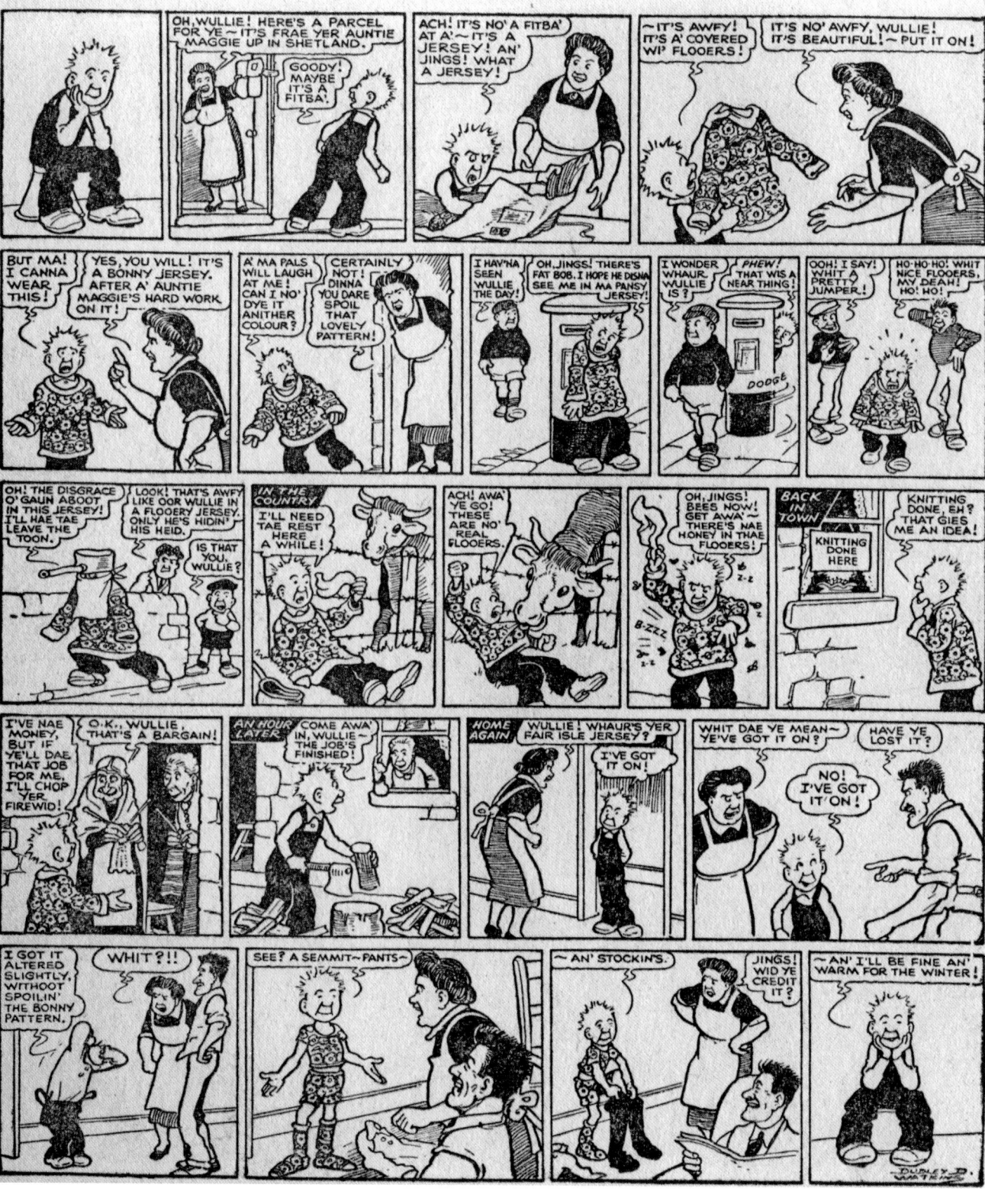

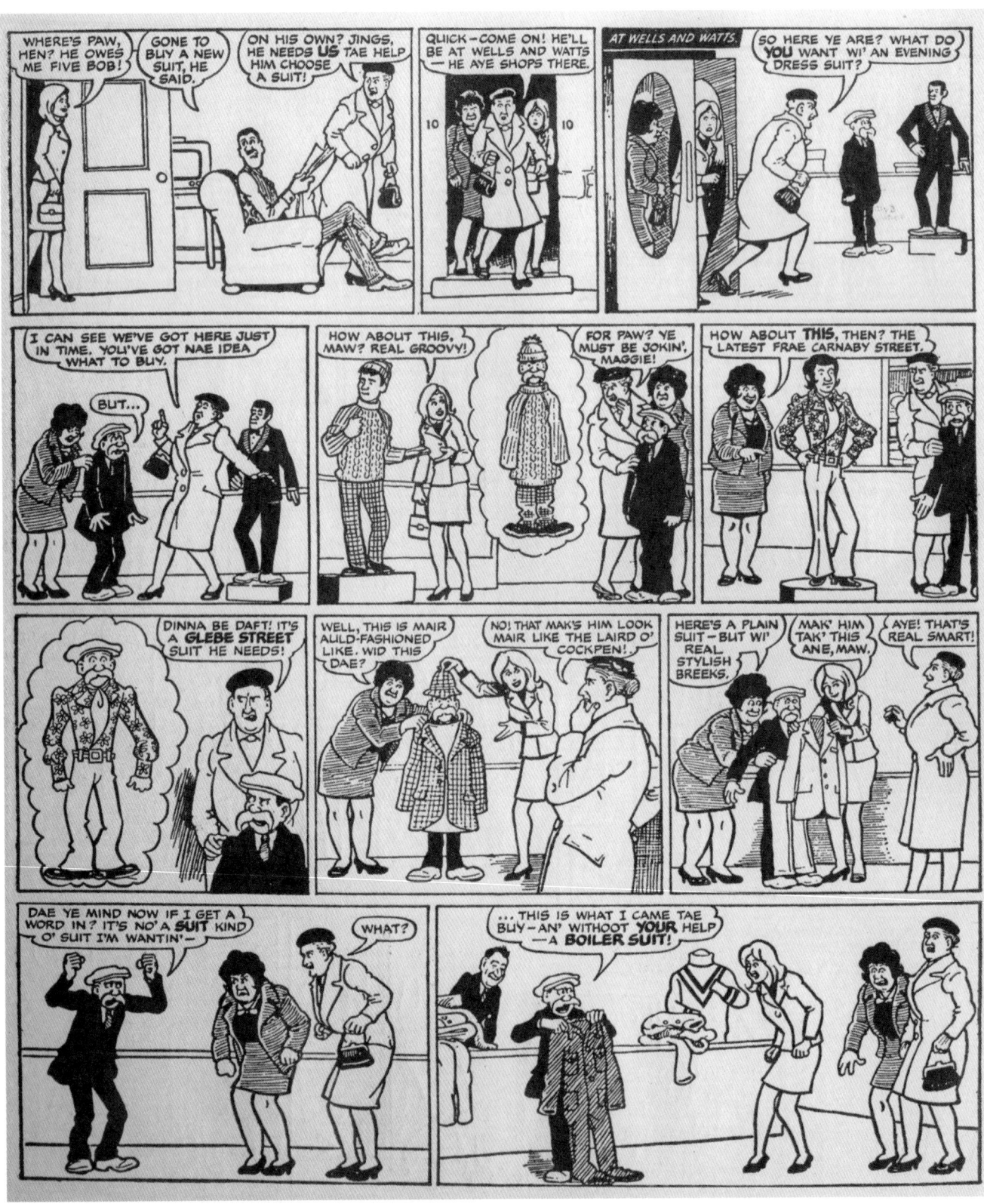

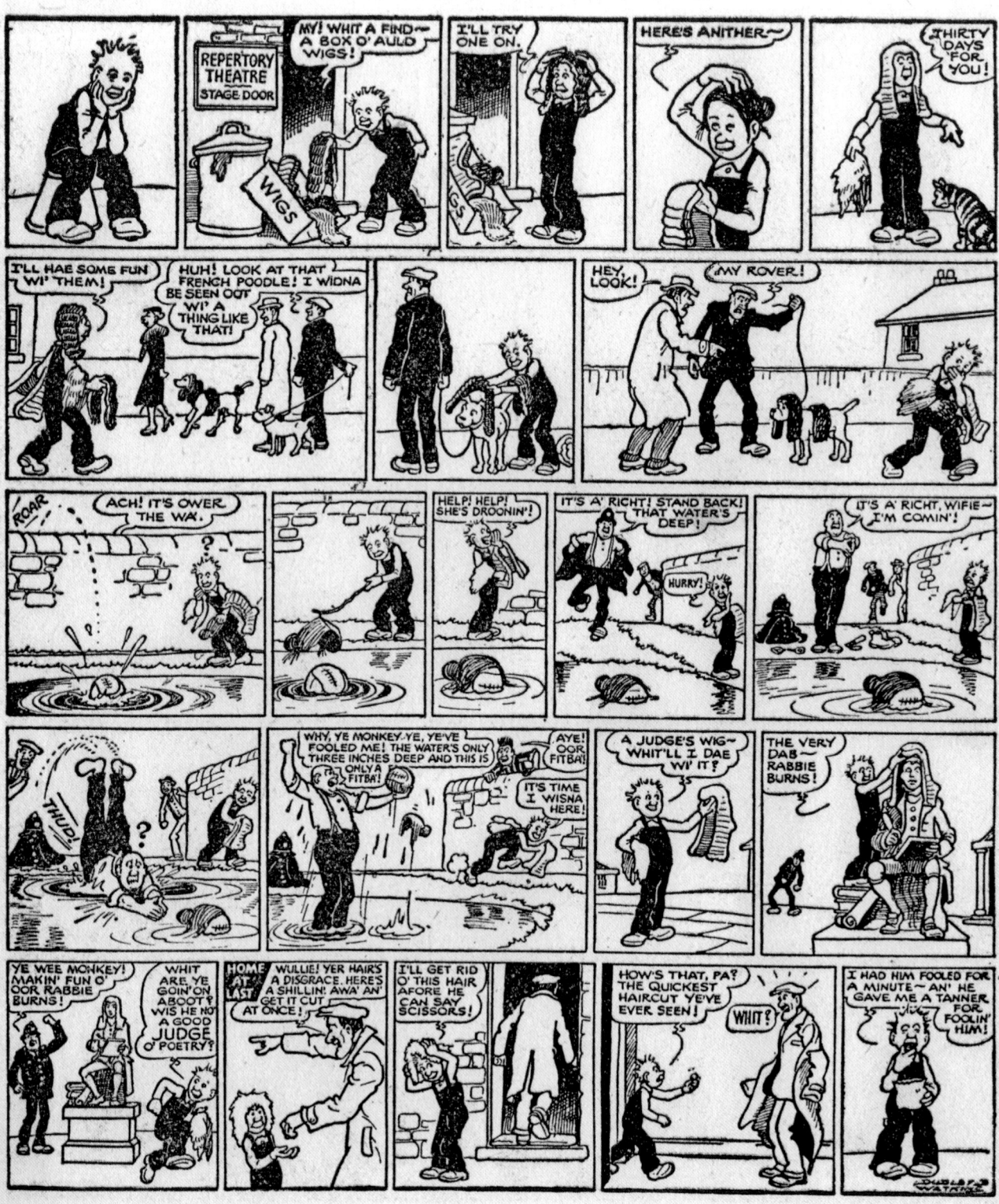

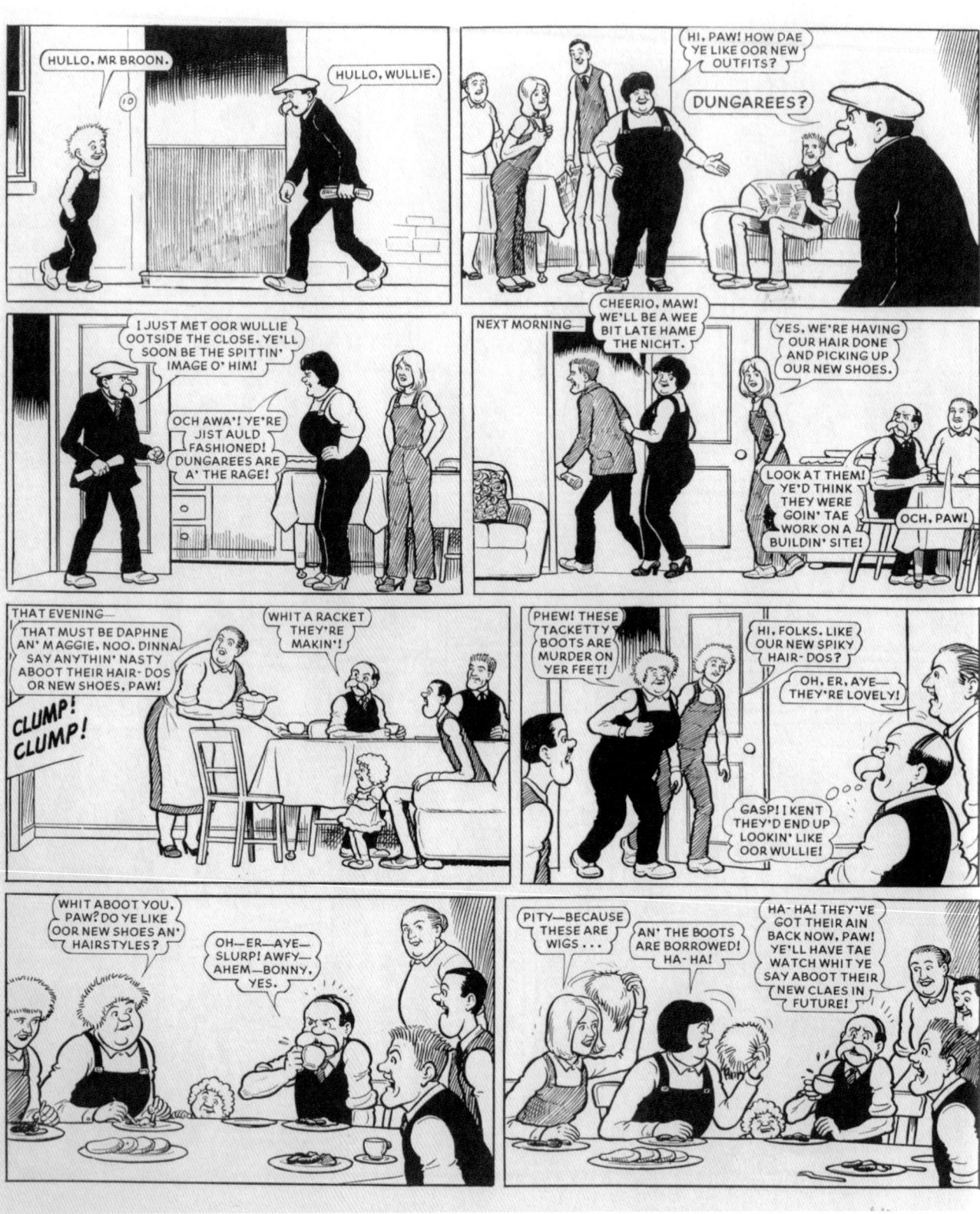

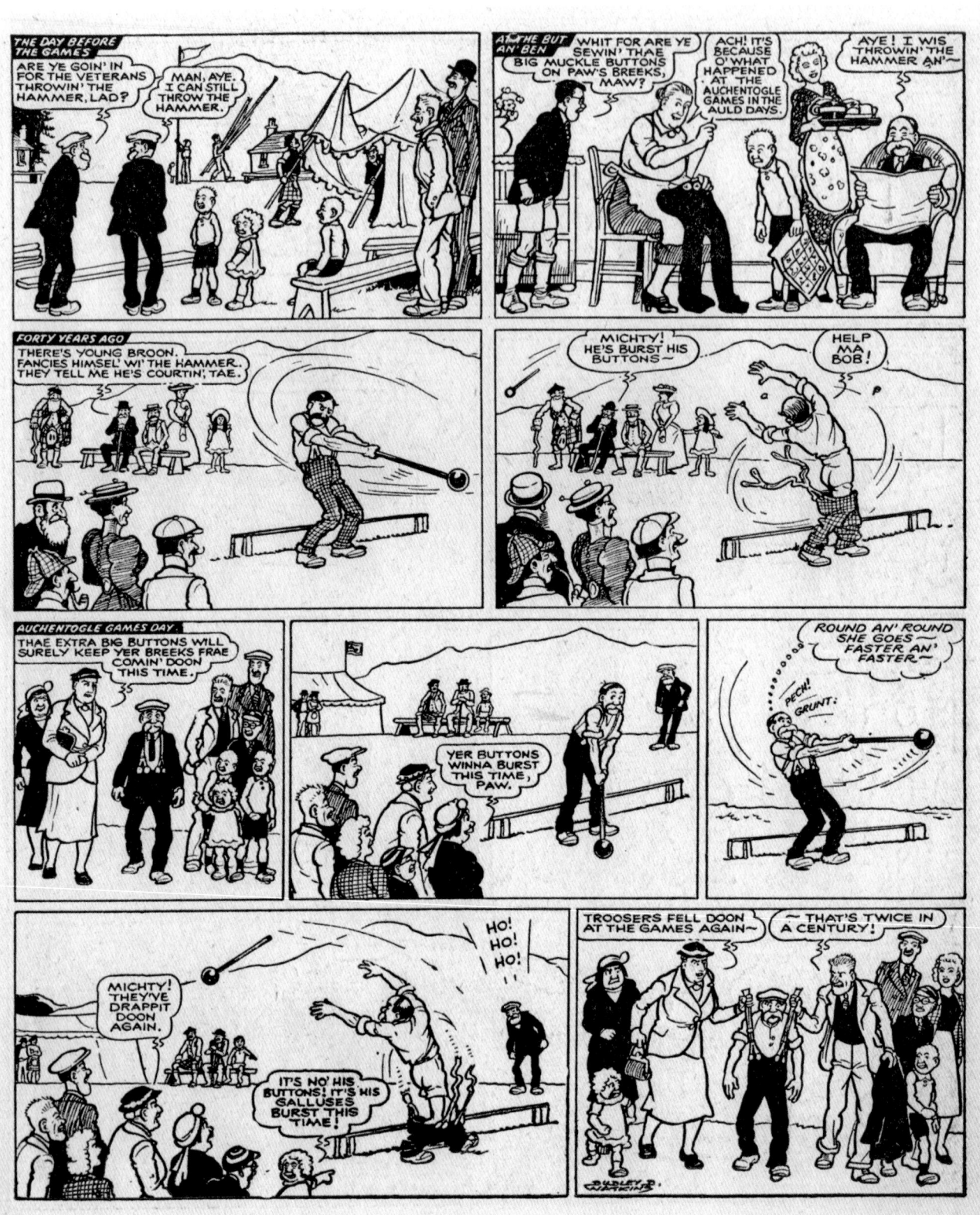

Fashion Faux Paw

Despite the young Broons keeping their finger on the fashion pulse over the years, one family member often stumbled into bad luck wherever style trends were concerned.

Unlucky in Love

Relationships were central to the humour in both Oor Wullie and The Broons. Oor Wullie spent many a day avoiding the affections of his female classmates, whereas the young Broons were always looking for a new click, often causing rivalry between the siblings.

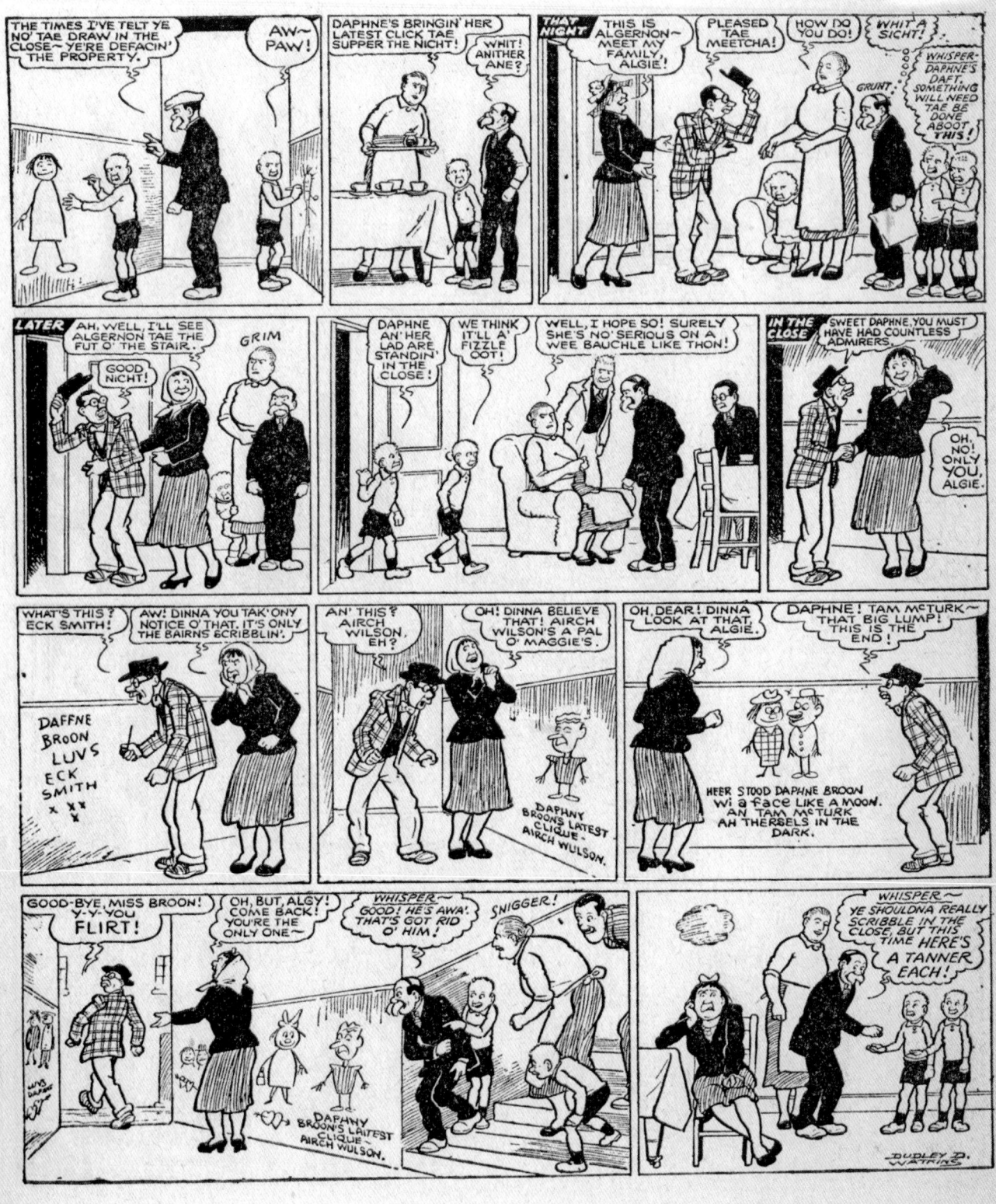

Friendship First

The Broons and Oor Wullie have made strong bonds with many supporting characters over the years. Wullie and his best friends – Soapy, Boab and Eck, went on many adventures. From camping in the wilderness to standing up to bullies, you could always count on Oor Wullie to be a loyal friend.

Despite their close friendships, it was not uncommon for the Broon siblings to quibble with each other or for Wullie and his pals to fall out.

Makin' Mischief

Having such close bonds with friends and family meant there was no end to The Broons' and Oor Wullie's mischievous potential, with an endless list of people to play pranks on. Creative ideas were key ingredients to a successful – and hilarious – comic strip!

The two young Broon twins were notorious for creating chaos for the Broon family,
often leaving Maw black affronted…

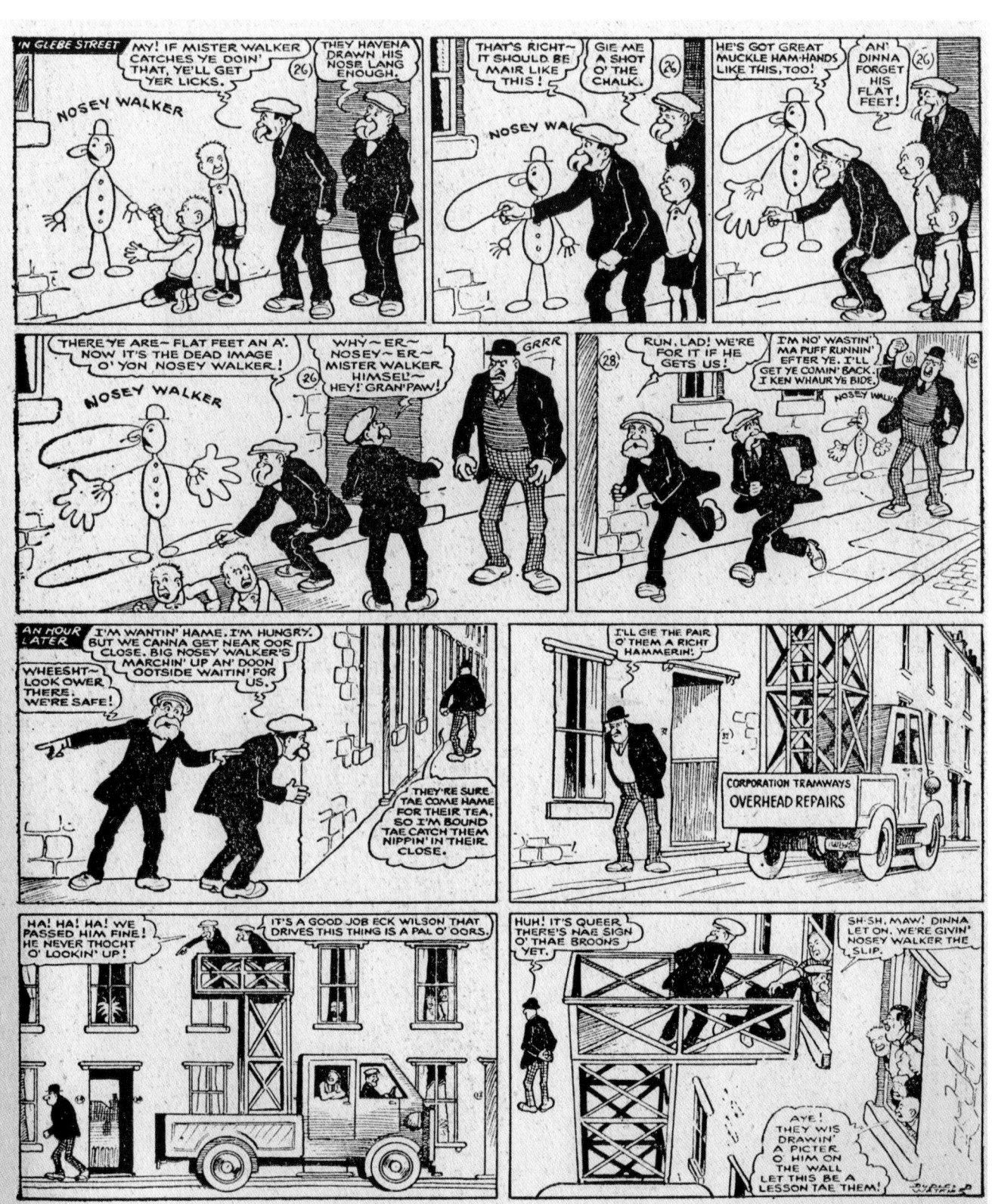

…but it's really no surprise when they have learned from the best pranksters in Auchentogle!

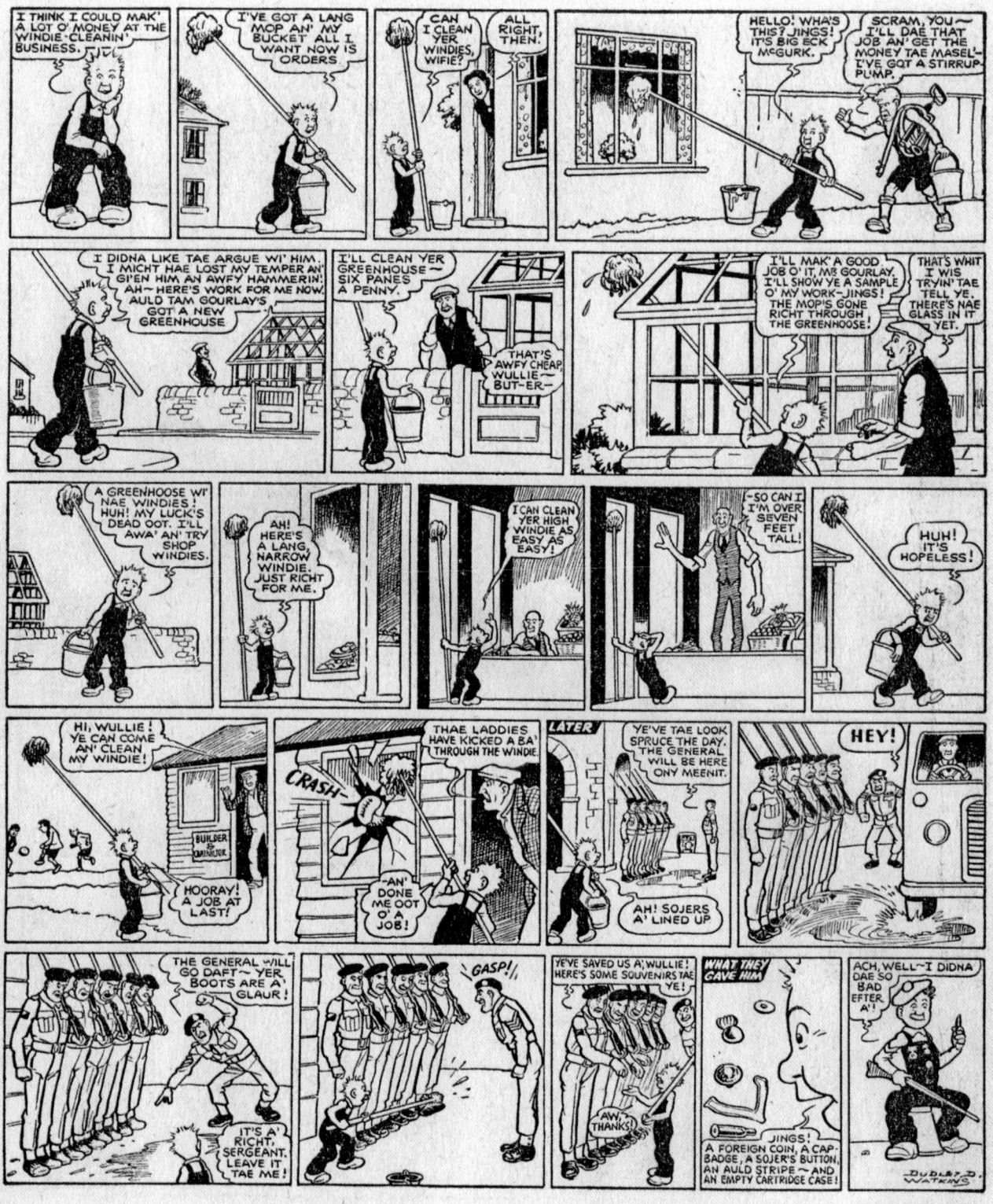

Name, Address and Whaur Do Ye Bide?

Oor Wullie's potential for making mischief was heightened by his friendship with local police officer, PC Murdoch. Wullie has been tormenting PC Murdoch since the 1940s, and they have since become fast friends.

Study Break

School has provided different opportunities for The Broons and Oor Wullie throughout the years. For the studious Horace Broon, it is where he is happiest. But the dungaree-clad lad from Auchenshoogle will use books for almost anything but studying.

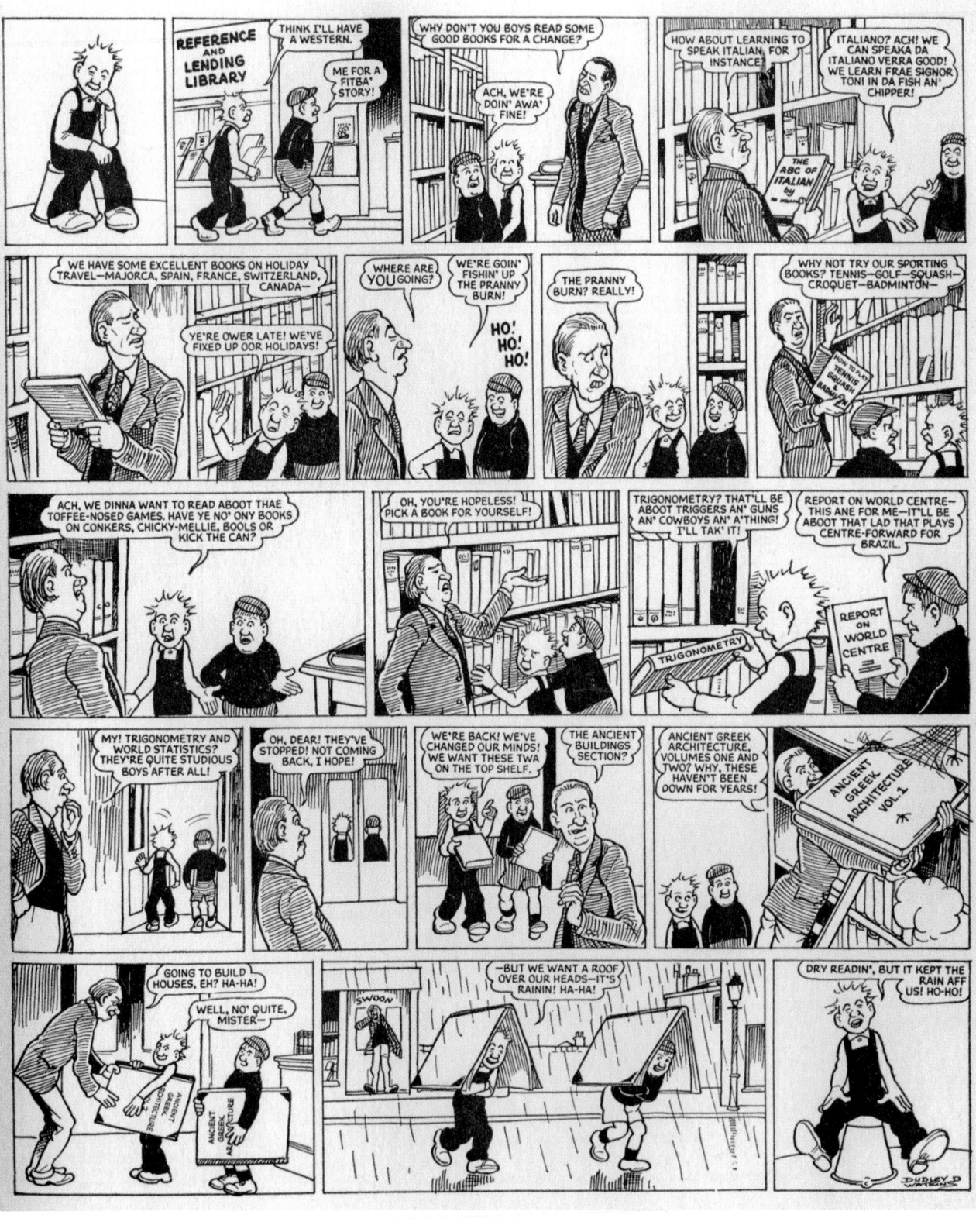

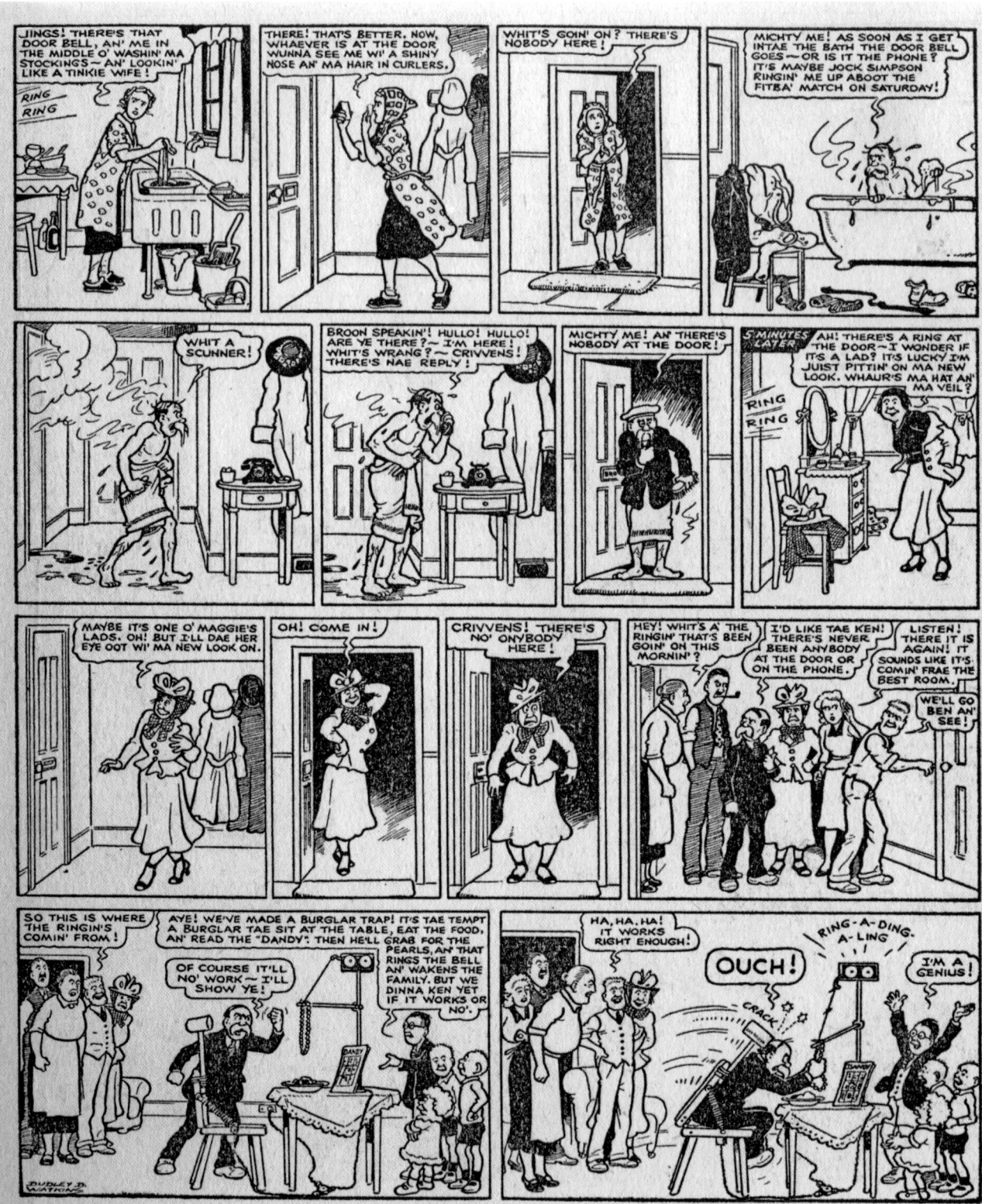

Home Comforts

Home really is where the heart is for The Broons and Oor Wullie. 10 Glebe Street has been the central point for the entire Broons family since the 1930s, with Maw as the proud head of the household. Even after a long day of mischief making, there's no place like home for Wullie to return to.

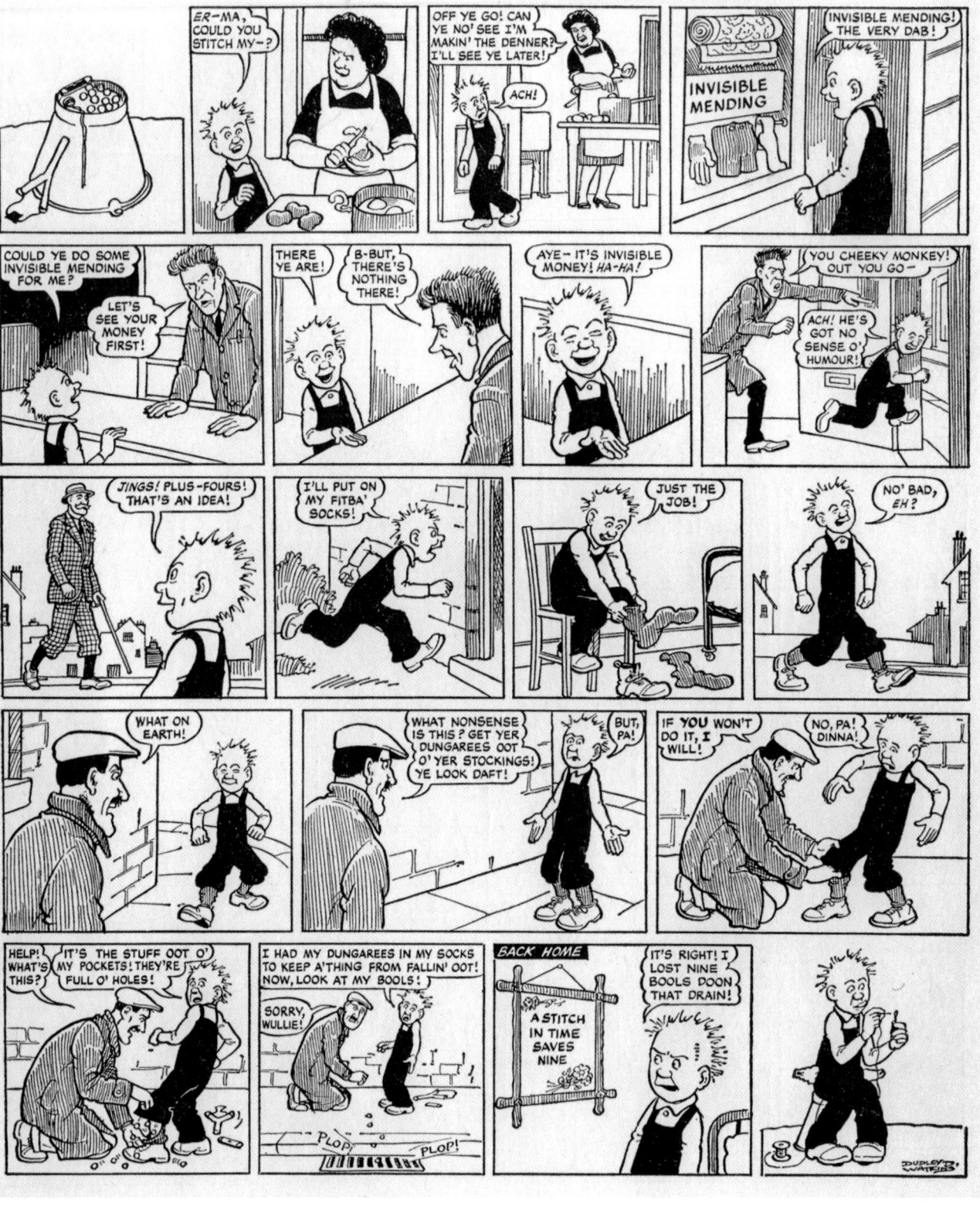

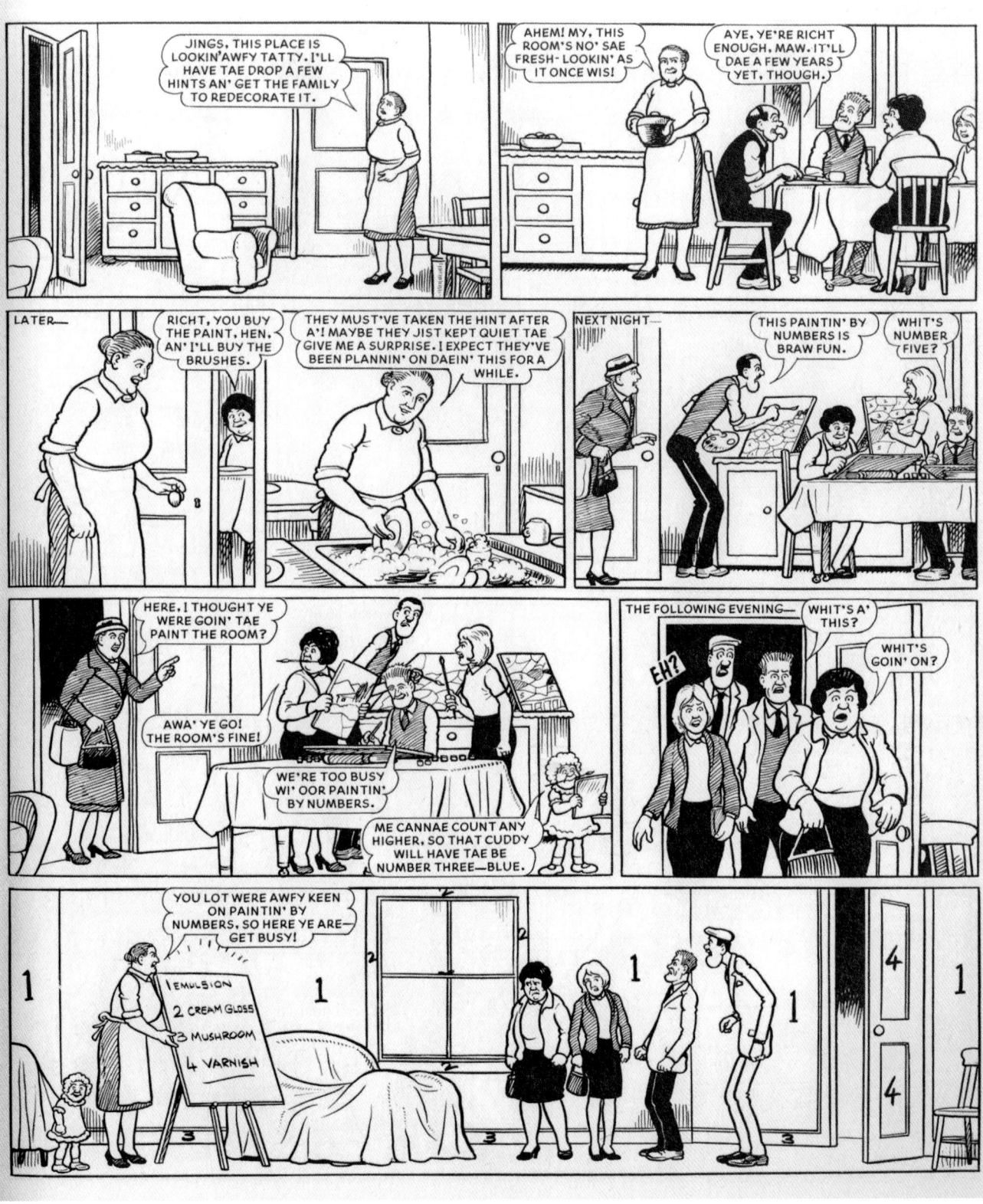

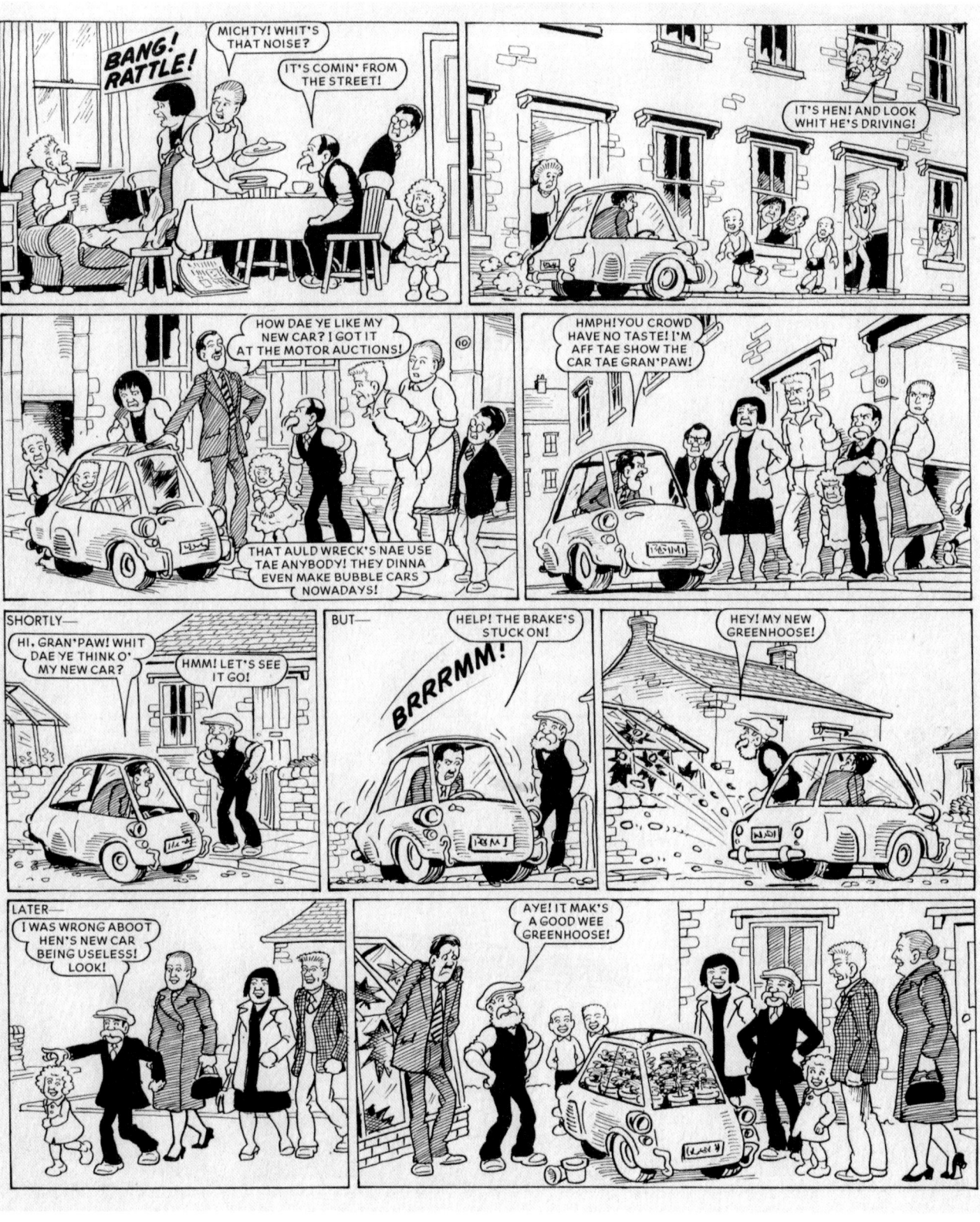

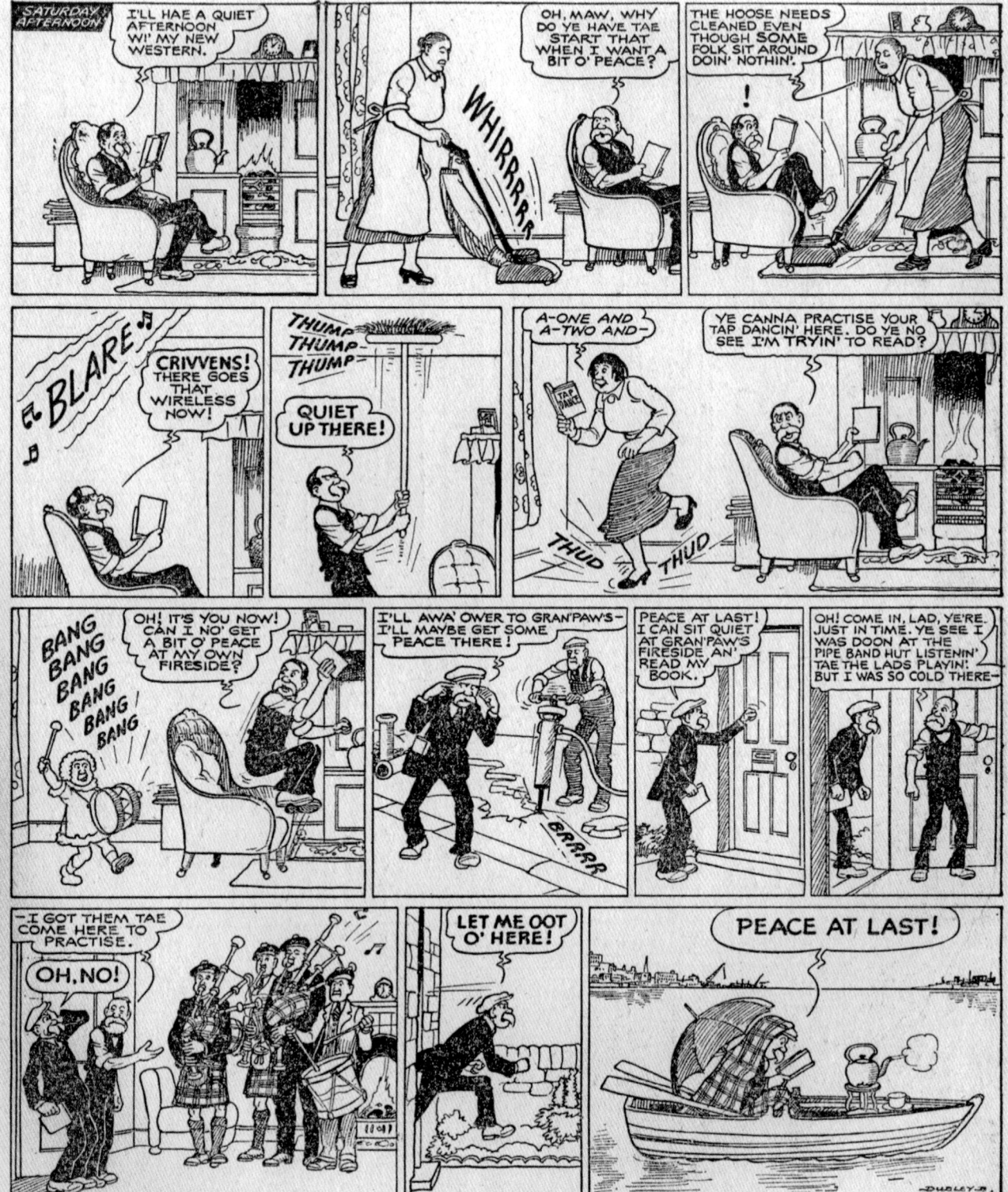

Musical Mayhem

Music has been an instrumental element in The Broons and Oor Wullie over the years, for bonding family and friends. Whether bringing the characters together for fun or ending in embarrassment, music has always been a great source of joy.

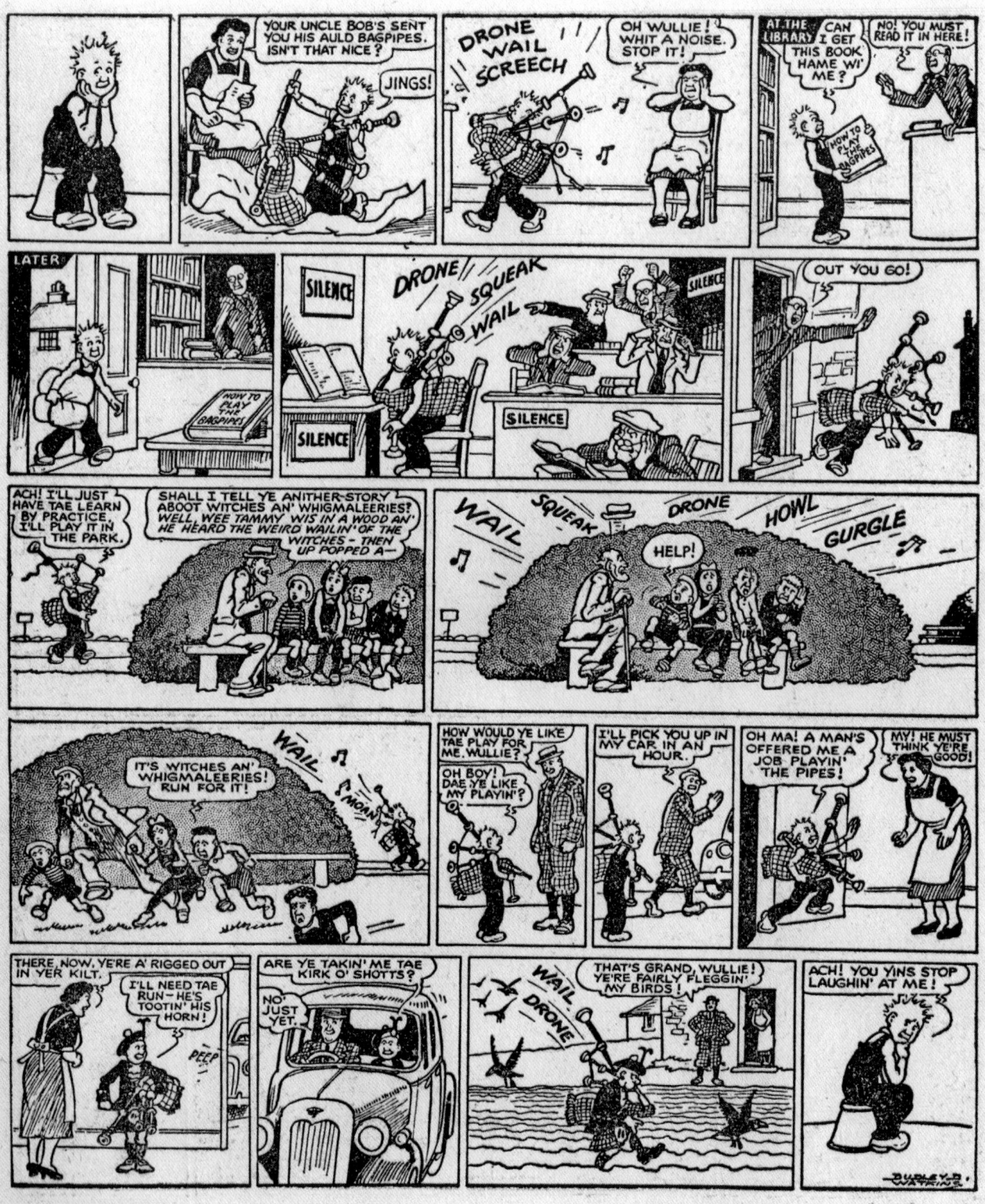

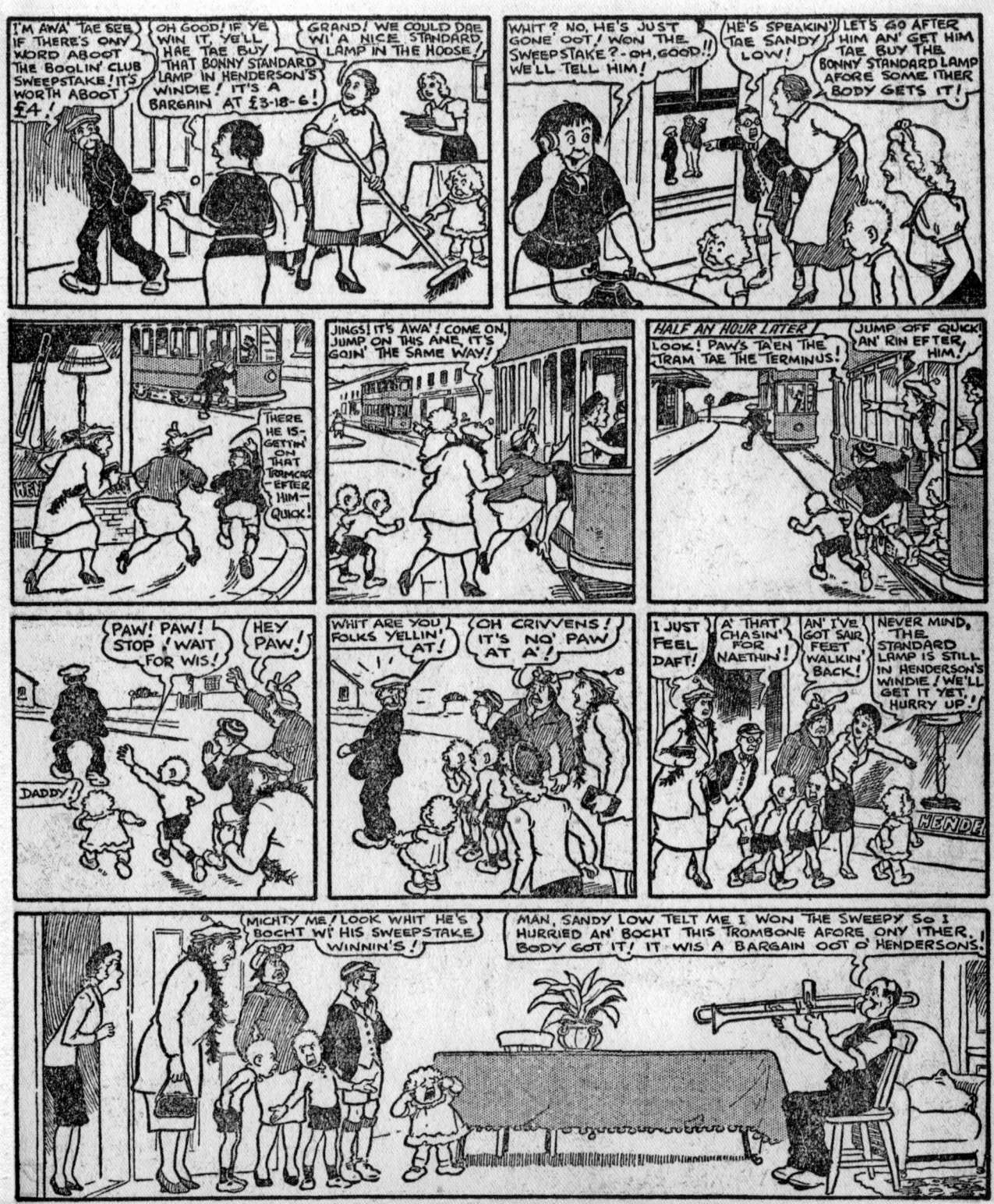

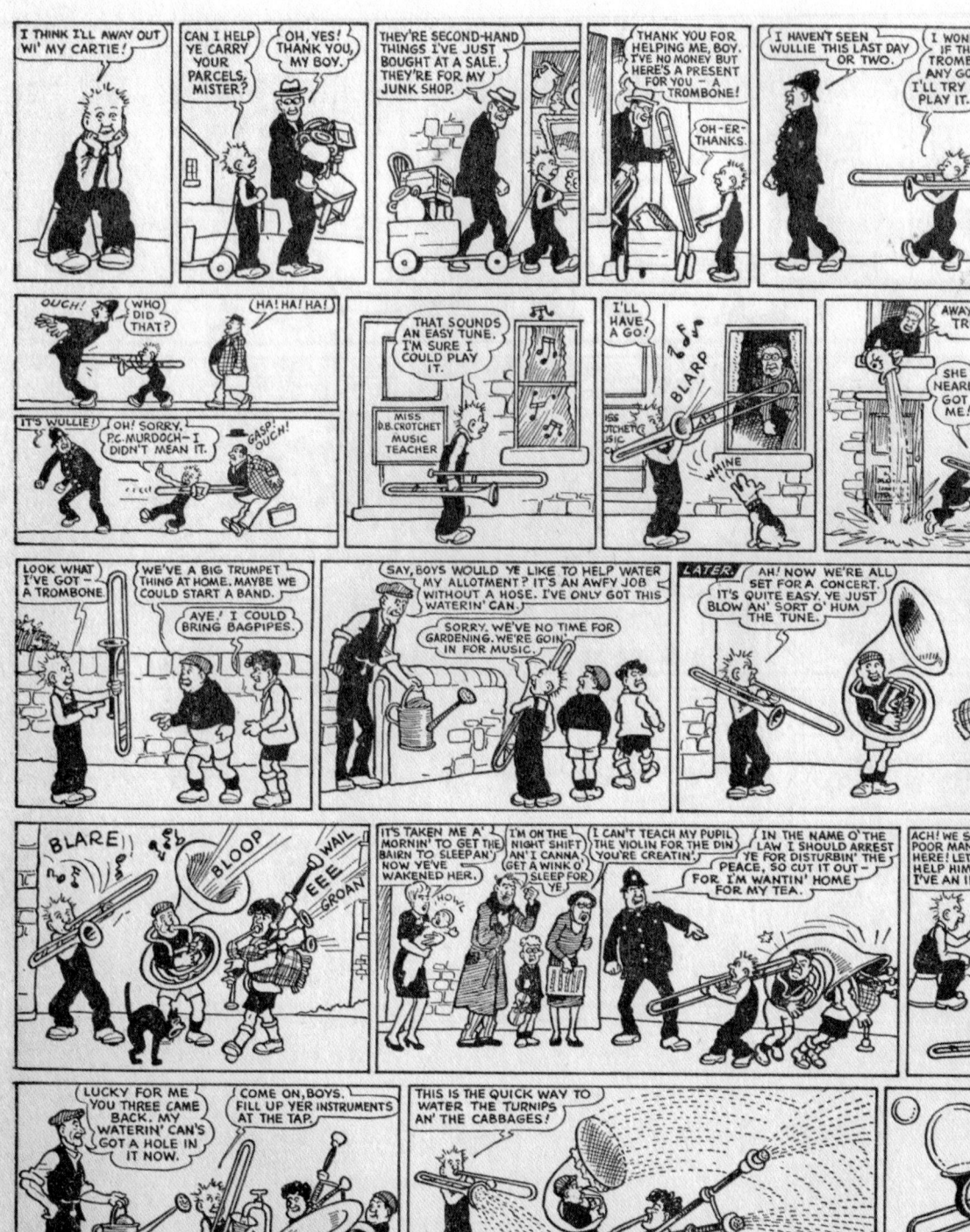

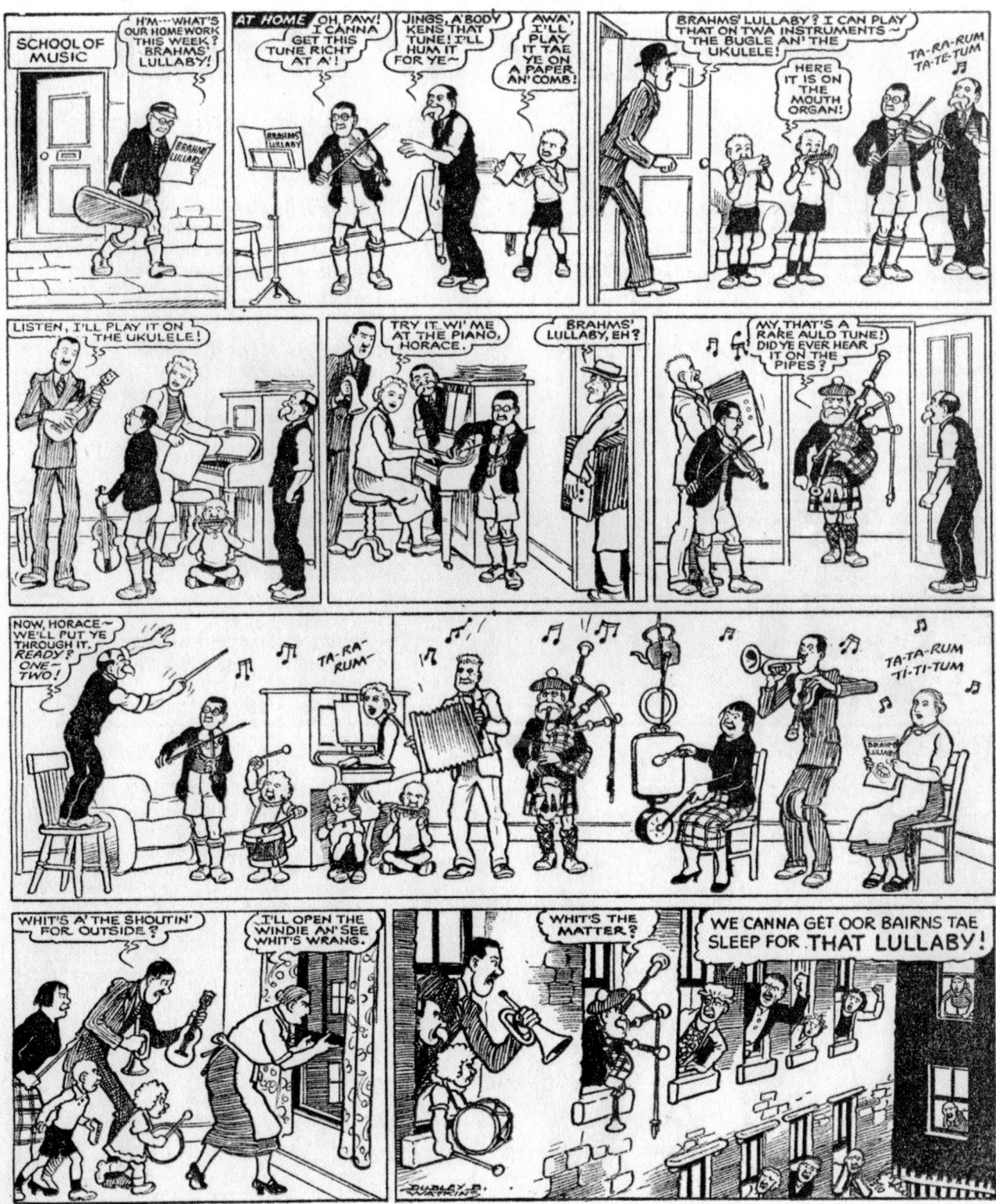

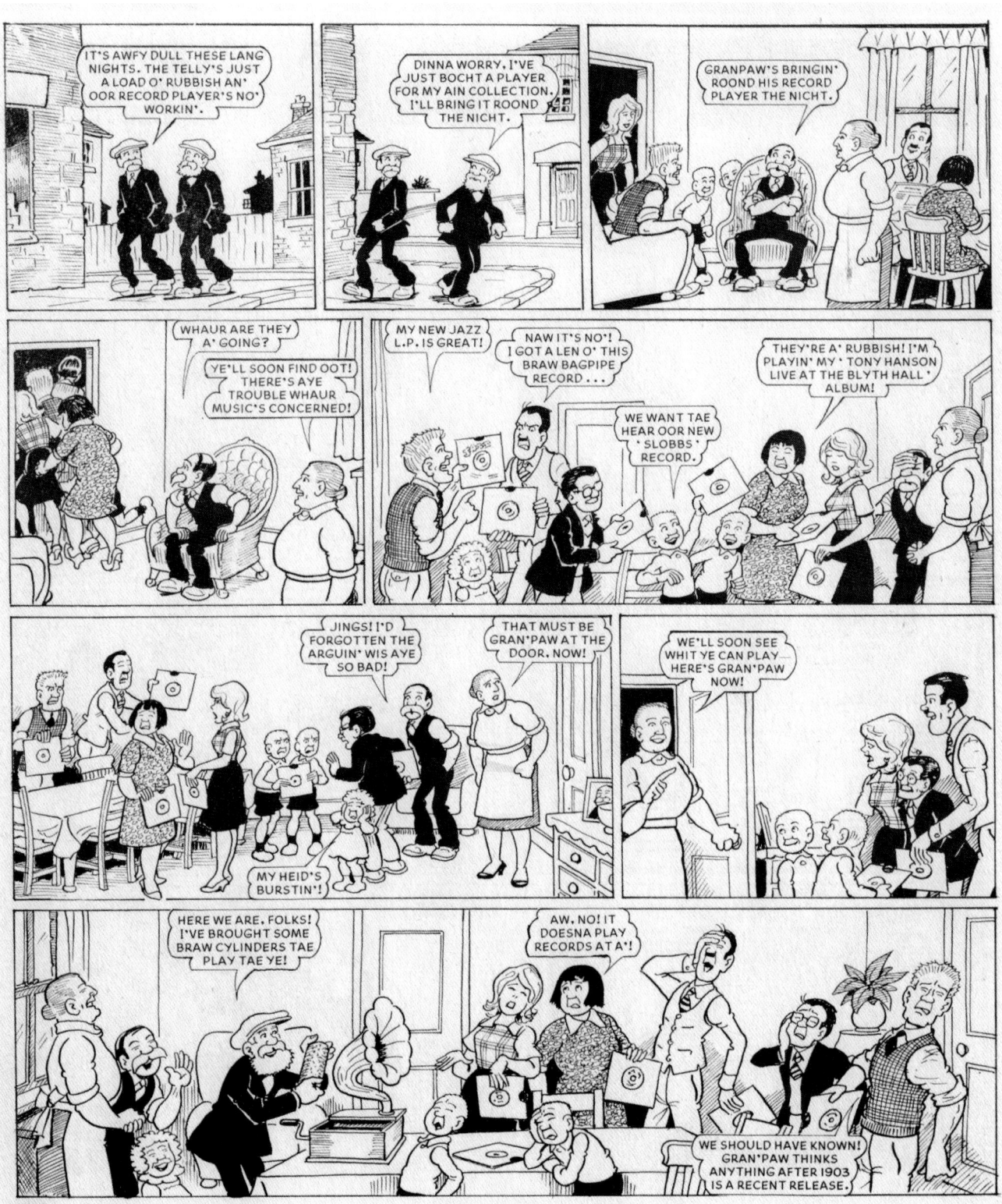

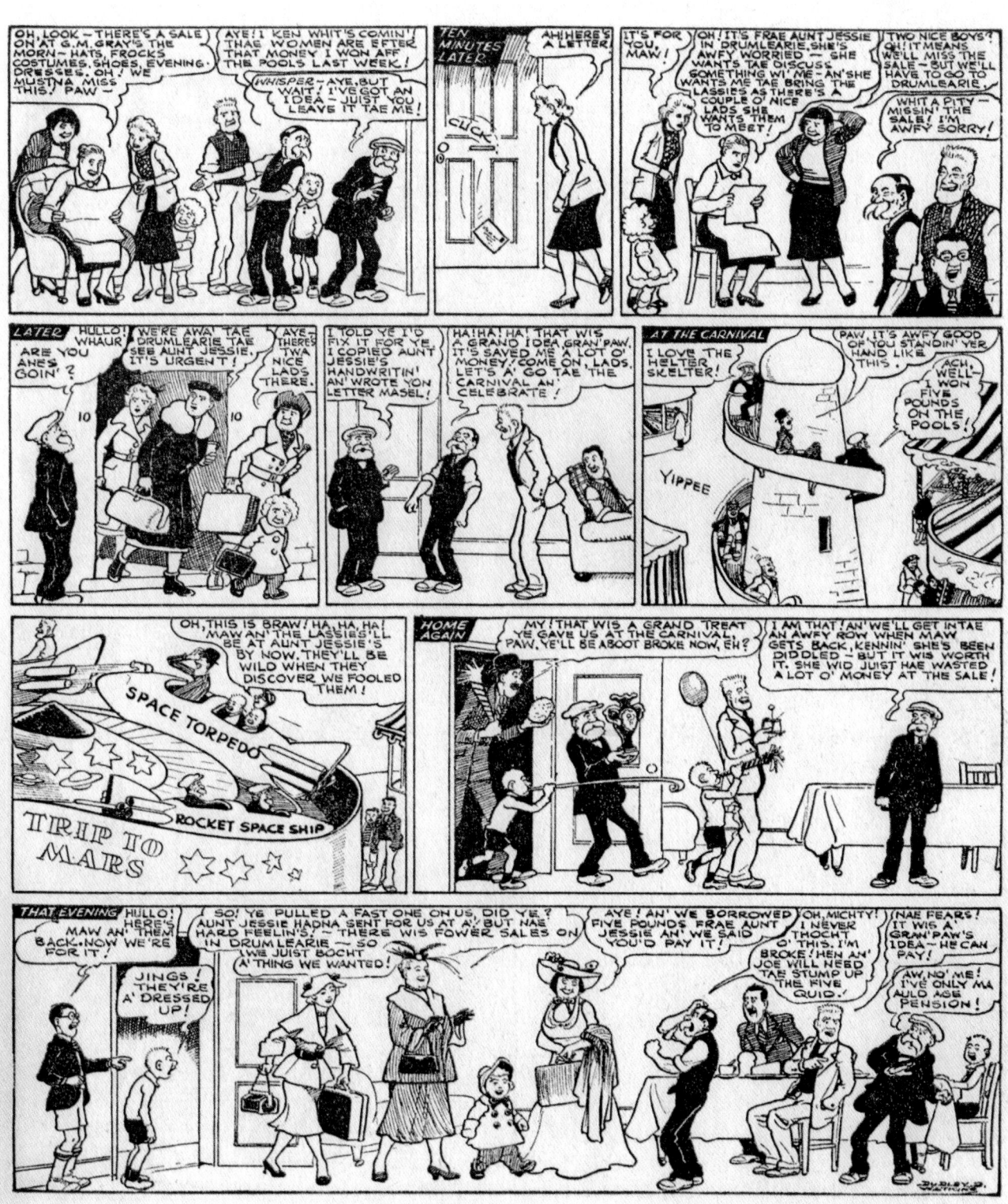

Holding the Purse Strings

The Broons have enjoyed many family outings since 1936, despite Paw's best efforts to keep a tight hold of his money. Paw's cheap daytrips often ended in embarrassment for him, and laughter for the rest of the family.

Even Oor Wullie tries his hardest to earn some extra pocket money.
He has tried his hand at many money making schemes over the decades.

Sign of the Times

The Broons and Oor Wullie have tried their best to keep as up-to-date as possible with popular trends. From fashion statements to the peak popularity of Grease, these comic strips have remained relevant by acknowledging recent events.

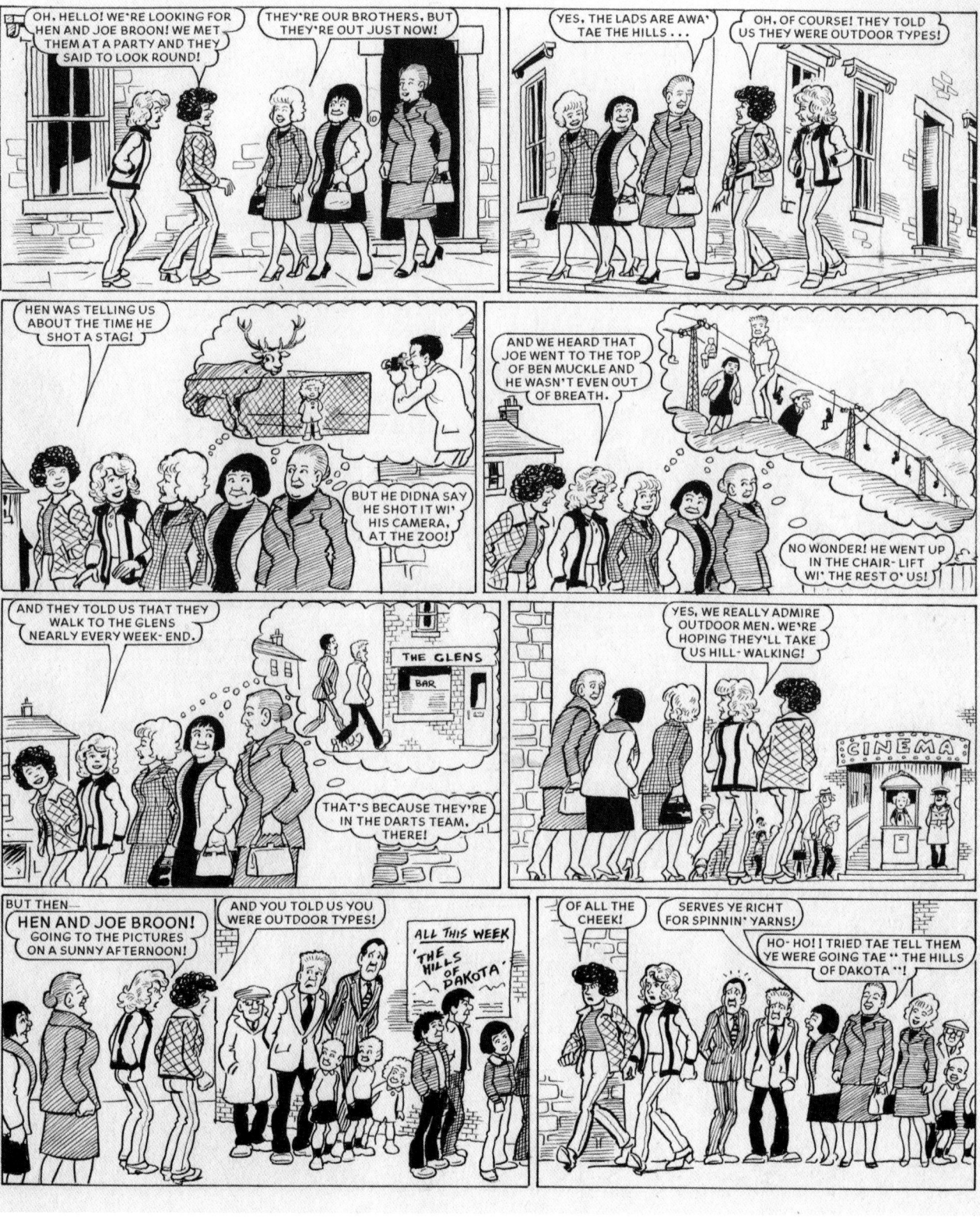

It is even possible to argue that The Broons have sometimes been ahead of their era. In this strip from 1943, Paw and Granpaw accidentally take a selfie.

The clearest example of The Broons and Oor Wullie's acknowledgement of the world around them is their involvement in the war effort. Desperate to play soldiers, the strips often saw Wullie do his part on the home front and even being evacuated to the countryside. Hen and Joe Broon fought on the front lines and often surprised their family with letters and home visits.

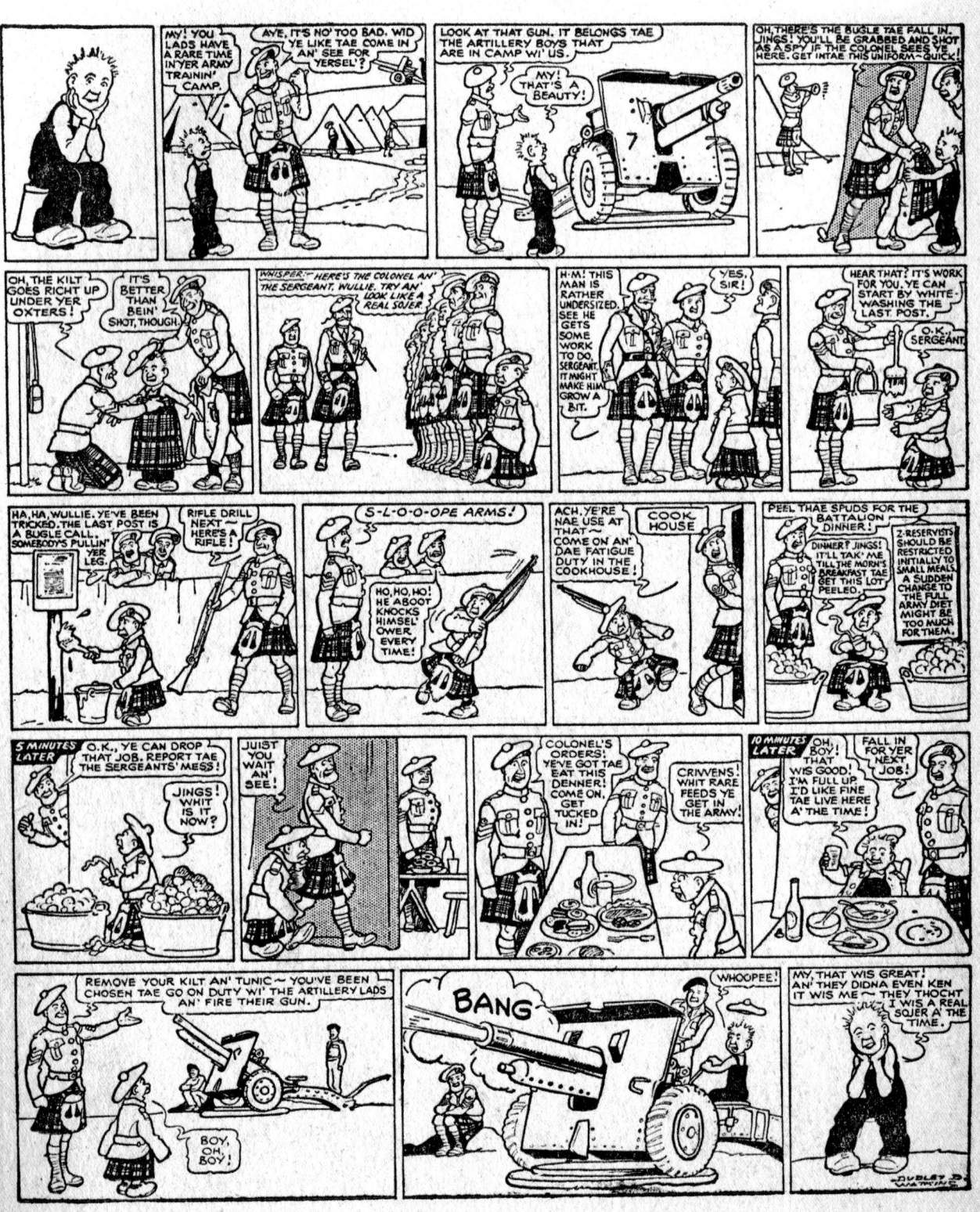

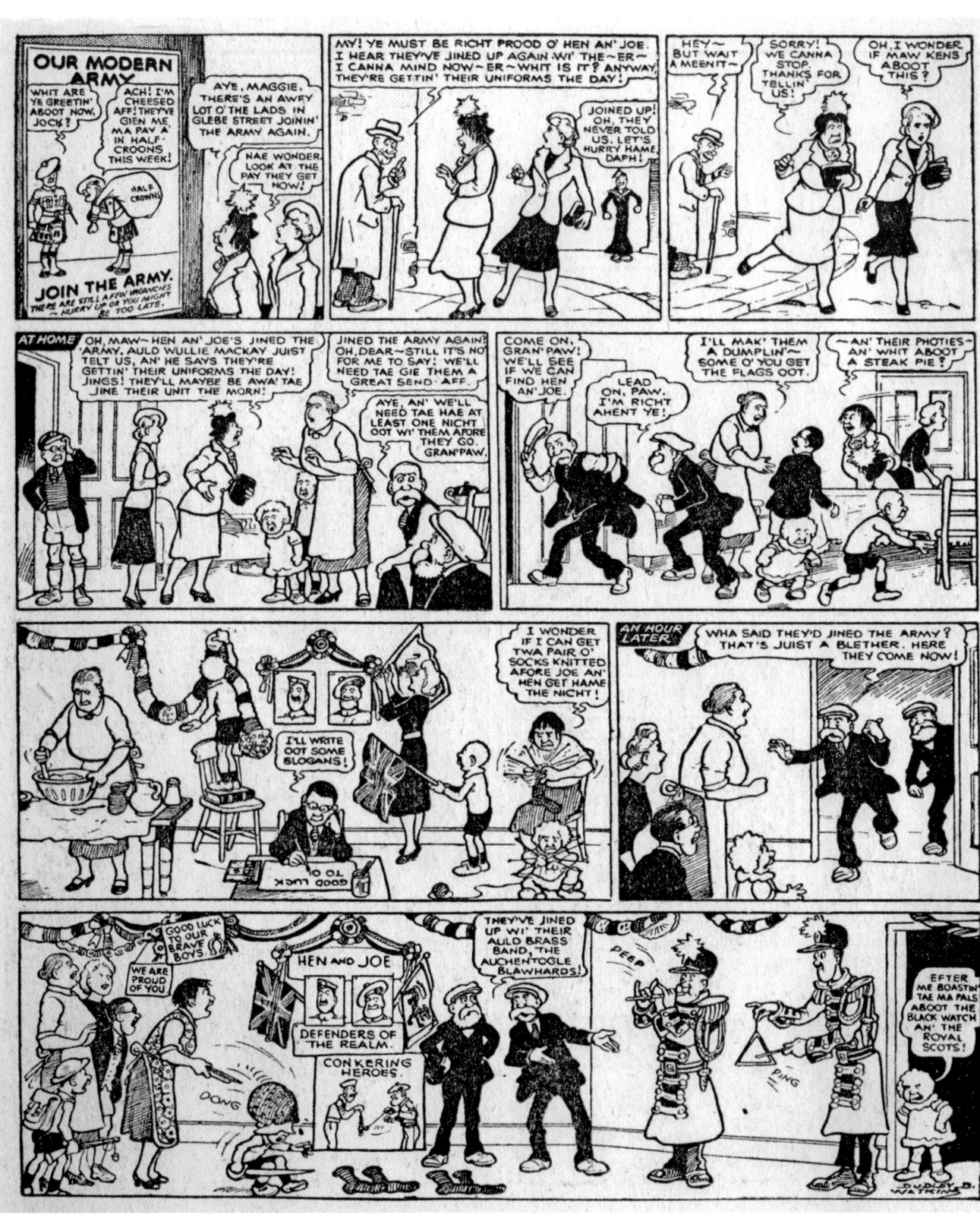

Family Matters

Throughout eighty years of change, one thing has remained consistent for The Broons and Oor Wullie: the importance of family. With their hearts firmly in the right place, their misfortune often stems from an attempt to do something caring for others.

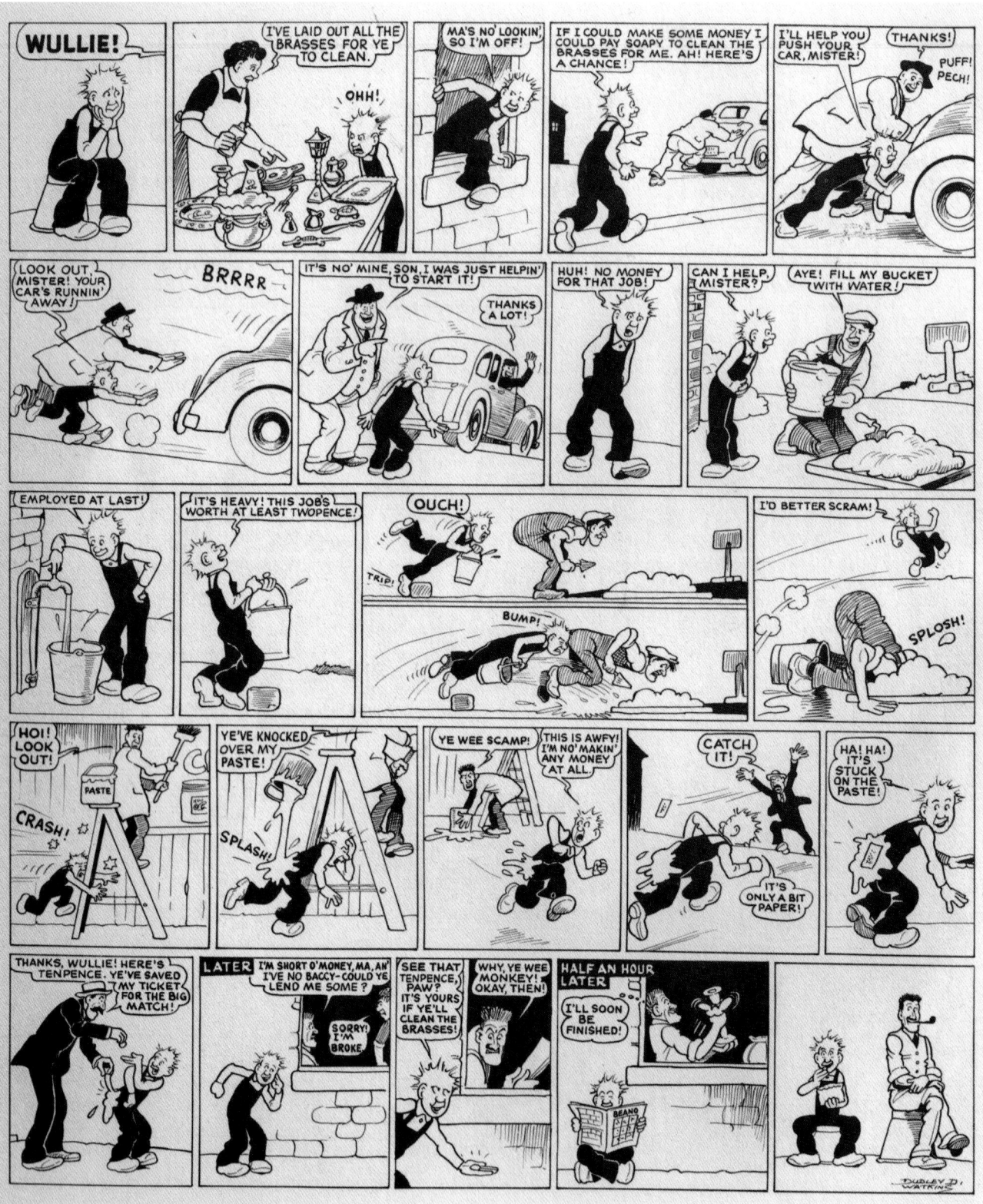

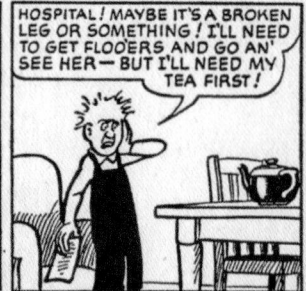

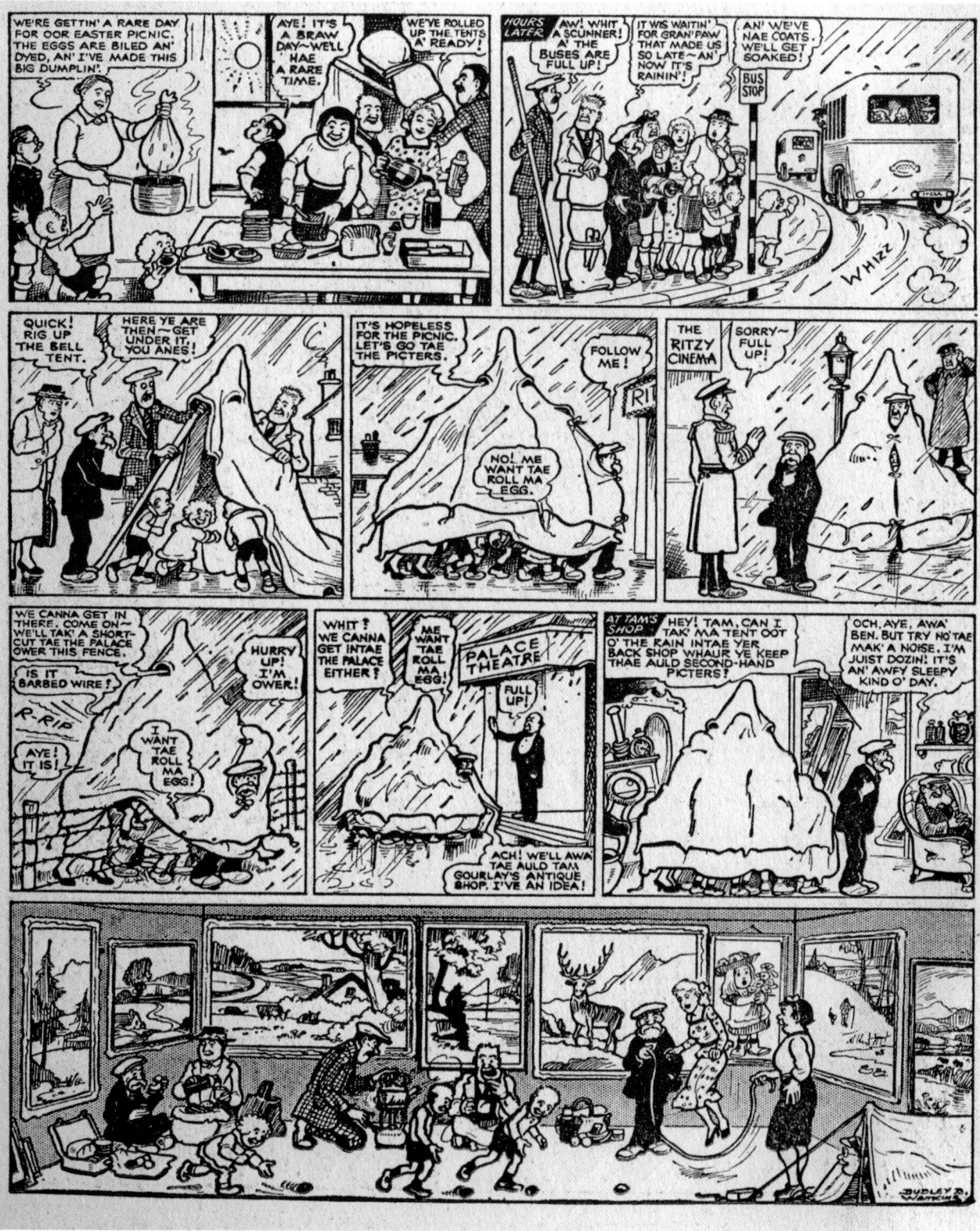

The Broons and Oor Wullie have endured a lot of change over the past eight decades. From world conflict to popular trends, the wee dungaree-clad laddie and the Glebe Street family have continued to thrive. This is partly due to the comfort the comic strips create, preserving time and lamenting the importance of community, family and friendship. But it is also solidified by the strips' ability to embrace change, acknowledging local and global events. By combining the old with the new, The Broons and Oor Wullie have become iconic figures in Scotland's comics history.

Of course, the key ingredient to The Broons and Oor Wullie's lasting appeal through the years is their warmth and ability to laugh with each other. Whether it be through fashion, mischief, school, or at home, these characters have created a sense of familiarity by resembling the ordinary family, often stumbling into extraordinary situations. Their ability to take each day in their stride, laughing along the way, turns situations we are all so familiar with into great adventures!

These classic strips have demonstrated the lasting appeal of these characters, who have many laughs together ahead of them yet.